Sex: the manual

Anne Hooper
Illustrations by Claudia Schenk
●●●ellipsis

First published 2001 by

•••ellipsis, 2 Rufus Street, London N1 6PE

EMAIL ...@ellipsis.co.uk

www.ellipsis.com

ISBN 1 84166 064 7

Printed and bound in Hong Kong

•••ellipsis is a trademark of Ellipsis London Limited

British Library Cataloguing in Publication Data: a CIP record for this publication is available from the British Library

For a copy of the Ellipsis catalogue or information on special quantity orders of Ellipsis books please contact sales on 020 7739 3157 or sales@ellipsis.co.uk

Contents

'Thought is a physical phenomenon'
  Mr Henry Marsh, neurosurgeon at Atkinson Morley hospital,
  London, 2001

Introduction

Have you ever asked yourself what is abnormal about fucking in the streets? Or wondered why people who choose not to have sex often get turned into a public joke? Where do our attitudes to sex originally come from? And is it appropriate that we should live by them without questioning them? Isn't it just possible that the ideas we accept as 'sexually normal' might actually be harming us?

This manual will start you thinking differently about your sexual attitudes, about your ideas of what is right and wrong. These ideas are not the big moral issues such as those concerning homosexuality or abortion but the most personal, intimate issues of all – those concerning our deepest being – the gritty dilemma of how we are in bed. How we feel as we wind our legs around another's; whether we dare to look a sex partner in the eye as we fuck; if we feel so free as we twist and writhe that we know we could do anything with this lover; these are examples of how we *can* be. As you read these examples, you may realise that such feelings do not always come to you automatically. You may reflect that life's grim experience means it is very hard even to trust *yourself* enough to look a partner straight in the eye during sex, let alone trust *them*.

Human beings have made a fetish of sex

Somewhere along the line, the idea evolved that sex should be done in private and that anything which offers ideas about public sex, such as public nudity for example, should be made unacceptable. The prohibitions on sex go even further – prescribing how sex should be done, what is good sex and what sexual failure. Instead of simply getting on with sex when the mood takes us, we have made a fetish of it.

So what's wrong with fetishes? Nothing, provided we feel comfortable with them and hurt nobody else with our predilections. But the upshot of our contemporary sexual system is that we feel controlled in bed; indeed, we believe we *are* controlled. If we do not reach orgasm, we believe we are failures; if we find it hard to sustain an erection, this becomes a reflection of our effectiveness in the world; if we climax too fast, we feel out of control. The layer upon layer of fetish wrapping coiled about us make it ridiculously difficult to take on board a simple fact – that *sex is what we make of it*. It is perfectly possible to construct sex – any sex -- as a positive or negative experience. It is not sex itself which is positive or negative, however wonderful or distressing a particular encounter may be, it is how we choose to feel about it.

Most of us have no idea that there is any choice involved here. We think that to be miserable in certain circumstances is logical. That is because we are not yet able to see a bigger picture. We cannot, so far, step outside the system of beliefs about sex that we imbibed during our 'civilised' childhood in order to understand that this system of control is only one of many. The reality is that we have a choice of systems.

Calming your sex attitudes down

Here's where this manual comes in. It will start you thinking about your sexual attitudes, specifically about the unconscious ideas you hold regarding what is right and wrong, so that you can at least progress to contemplating other approaches. By doing so you may be able to see that your present sexual situation has value of its own, even if by generally accepted measurements it seems distressing. You may thus learn to feel better about how sex is for you.

But I hope to go further than making you feel better. By bringing a more creative attitude to your sexual relationship I hope you may discover that you can tackle a number of sexual difficulties, which previously proved intransigent. This is not a 'how-to' sex manual in the mechanical tradition although some 'how-to' is included. Each chapter in this book will introduce ideas about *how to regard specific aspects of sex differently*. By reframing your ideas, I hope you will calm down your sex attitudes enough to see your personal strengths and values emerge from the present-day fog of stress and unhappiness.

I make use of ideas drawn from evolutionary psychology, a new school of thought for understanding human behaviour which draws together ideas from cognitive psychology and evolutionary biology. Evolutionary psychology is still developing and many scientists and anthropologists do not agree with its ideas, but that doesn't mean that it isn't healthy to rethink your position on sex – pun definitely intended. This book is all about *rethinking your position*.

Growing our beliefs

Where do ideas about sex come from?

The Viennese inventor of Adlerian psychology, Alfred Adler, believed that personality is shaped initially by our experience within the immediate family, later by the wider context of larger family and friends, and finally by the outside world. Today we might add a fourth dimension to the growth of personality by including global influences, i.e. the impact of world-wide telecommunications that brings ideas and customs of almost every nation to our door.

Adler believed that humans have a basic drive towards gaining a sense of personal value, since our earliest experiences (as a baby) are of feeling small and weak in a world of giants. Out of this desire to feel strong comes the need to believe we are effective in this world and that other people see us and respect us as such. We begin to grow a belief system.

Sex and parents

So where does sex fit into this? We not only learn about the facts of life (and sex) from parents but we also see the example of warmth, trust and communication that they set. If we have parents who fight like mad but who then make it up, retire to the bedroom and come out the next day looking happy we learn that good sex is re-affirming. *Ergo* – sex is strengthening.

If our parents are able to be open about sex, to discuss it honestly with us when we are infants, by the time we grow up we feel reasonably comfortable with sex when we finally get to it. Interestingly, research shows that the more open a parent is able to be with children about sex, the older they are likely to be before having first-time sex, the more likely to use contraception and the less likely to conceive uninvited babes. The logic here is that knowing about sex allows us to feel secure and confident.

When sex is a strain

If sex is never discussed, and/or there is a sense of tension and strain between parents, young men and women grow up to believe that sex can be full of problems. This doesn't appear to put them off having sex but it does mean that they know less about it, less about their own sexual response and are much less confident as individuals. Conclusion – in the absence of information, and where there is a tense atmosphere concerning sex, we are forced to make up the facts for ourselves. What we imagine often causes us more stress than what we really know.

TIMID WOMEN

Many of the young women who used to take part in my sexuality workshops in the 1970s and 1980s found it difficult to experience orgasm partly due to a serious lack of personal self-esteem. These women regularly described fathers who were cold and distant and mothers who were timid, nervous and who found it impossible to stand up to their partner's bad temper and moods. In other words, stressful parental example and little sexual information can lead to unfulfilling sex lives.

Teaching orgasm

Hand in hand with parental influence goes positive social and sexual teaching. In the 1970s and 1980s very few women in my groups had ever been told about:

• taking time over beginning a sexual friendship;
• taking time over mutually discovering sex;
• how orgasm actually worked; or
• possessing a clitoris.

In the 2000s young men and women know rather more about sex than they did 25 years ago, thanks to the burgeoning of sexual advice in the media and also to the partial breakdown of inhibitions over discussion between parents and children. Yet many of today's budding sexual beings still don't appear to know that for sex to work well

← 4 inch →

chastity device for
husband when
away from home.

it helps to establish a caring, loving friendship. A Channel 4 television series on youth and sex in 2000 indicated that most of its young participants could talk to each other about sex but very few of them had done so with parents. Sharing of information did improve their friendships but it also led to some serious sexual mistakes which ended up with a pregnant 14-year-old.

Learning about anything from your peers has its pluses and minuses. The pluses are that you are likely to give and receive information on a level you can truly relate to and understand; the minuses are that the information itself may be faulty or biased in directions that prove uncomfortable or even emotionally harmful. The people featured were approaching sex at an extremely young age and didn't look particularly happy about their subsequent experience of it. They gave the impression that they expected sex to work at the push of a button and were surprised when it didn't.

Faulty facts

They knew how to do sex from receiving sexual ideas from their own age group but they didn't seem to know how to enjoy it. And what about those ideas? What about the concepts we take on board from parents, school, peers? Where do those ideas actually come from originally? I don't mean which textbook they came from. Nor do I mean which parent or teacher expounded them. I mean, where did the ideas actually originate?

Origins of sexual ideas

The answer is a simple one, say the socio-biologists. Sex is a human instinct. Penis and clitoris are equipped with amazing sensation that virtually compels individuals to explore, to use their amazing primate intelligence and subsequently fit erection into vagina. Sex is also an animal instinct and the our ancestral cave-person, living alongside other species, was perfectly capable of seeing these other creatures mate and then transferring such visual information to his/her own species and following suit. The present-day experience of sex must therefore have had its origins in this early time and developed accordingly.

ANCESTRAL SEX

It's commonly believed that early man was naturally a premature ejaculator since it would have aided his survival in a cruel world to get sex over and done with fast. If you know that a sabre-tooth tiger might be hanging around the entrance to your cave, it's not a good idea to have your back turned for too long. So today's premature ejaculators, far from feeling ashamed of their sexual prowess, might feel proud that they are descended from 'true men' in an absolutely fundamental sense.

Cavemen who became impotent may well have been those who were stressed, diseased, ageing or just plain worn out.

It might have suited them to be forced to take a break from sex, regardless of their opinion in the matter; it might have suited their equally ageing partners; and it might have suited the quality of the resultant sperm, ensuring that below-par sperm did not result in below-par babies – we're talking gene transfer here.

Women can climax too

The notion that women didn't have orgasms was widely believed for years since, in evolutionary terms, there appeared to be no need for them. As recently as 1975 certain English doctors denied the possibility of female orgasm on the grounds that as women didn't ejaculate, orgasm was impossible. Now that it has been proved beyond doubt that women do experience the big O, biologists and anthropologists have been dreaming up evolutionary reasons why.

One explanation is that at the moment of orgasm the cervix (the entrance to the uterus) dips and bathes in the pool of ejaculated semen lying there inside the vagina, thus expediting the journey of sperm towards ovum. *Ergo*, women were equipped with orgasm in order to perpetuate the species. I would hazard a guess that since a cavewoman may well have been subject to the rapacious sexual advances of many males, it may be that the experience of orgasm favoured the sperm of the men who most turned her on. Her babies would be more likely to be those of the man with whom she could develop the richest sexual relationship.

We have absolutely no idea about intimate relationships between such early men and women. However, all the new research into genetic identity and the brain seems to tell us that these ancient lovers were probably not that different from you and me. They didn't have much technology, they had an appalling struggle to survive in the wild, but their brains were probably not all that different. More about this later.

The evolutionary view

Charles Darwin, author of *On the Origin of Species* (1859) and *The Descent of Man and Selection in Relation to Sex* (1871), and probably the most influential man of past and present centuries, came up with two major theories (at least) about evolution. The first was the idea of *natural selection*. The second was that of *sexual selection*.

The compulsive genes

The theory of *natural selection* has it that human brains, and therefore human beings, evolved through the survival of the fittest. In other words, if you could survive well enough and long enough to father or mother as many children as possible, those children were most likely to be survivors in their own right and to continue to pass on your genes. Your line would thus survive, thanks to its constant and ultimate fitness at adapting and coping with the hideously difficult circumstances into which you were born.

The men and women who coped less well were more likely to be snuffed out by a falling tree, eaten by a predator or, most important of all, kicked down to a lower position in society and therefore given less access to mates. On these bases there are probably not a lot of descendants of the less able alive and well in the world today.

Why are we more evolved than the apes?
The problem with the theory of natural selection left on its own is that it doesn't explain the very important differences between man and the other great primates. Chimpanzees, gorillas and other great apes have also survived and share 98 per cent of their DNA with us, their cousins. Yet they didn't make the great leap whereby their brains enlarged and they developed the major and detailed skill of speech. (They may be in the process of doing that now. But only with help from us. They haven't done it on their own.)

What is more, the creative arts developed alongside speech. From a purely biological point of view the great arts seemed to be useless – a kind of sideline that is a dead end from the point of view of survival. One biological argument suggested that because our enlarged brains gained the ability to learn new things, all these extras were merely 'frosting on the cake'. Yet today new ideas about

sexuality and creativity are suddenly hitting the headlines. I quote here Geoffrey Miller who, in his book *The Mating Mind,* makes a compelling argument for the additional evolution of the second type of selection coined by Darwin, *sexual selection.*

Sexual selection is not quite what you might imagine. It doesn't simply mean that men and women choose the partner who most turns them on and so passes the most sexually successful genes on down through that particular line. It means a lot more besides. It offers an explanation of why human beings write, paint, think, tell stories, or do anything that might interest and intrigue others. It may be connected to the sexual hoops we put ourselves through in the here and now. It certainly offers explanations for our choices to confine ourselves to one mate instead of many, or at least make a show of doing so. It might underlie the fact that we often believe we ought to do sex in a certain way, in a certain room, with or without clothes, in a 'good' or a 'bad' fashion. And since these beliefs may be responsible for undermining our instincts about sex, it's worth taking a look at their origins.

WHY THE PEACOCK SPREADS HIS TAIL Geoffrey Miller explains his point through a description of a peacock and why it evolved its gorgeous tail. Such a huge appendage might well be seen, from the perspective of survival of the fittest, as an evolutionary disadvantage since it must mean that a peacock would find it exceedingly difficult to flee from a predator. Since peacocks remain with us today, there must be some other advantage to be derived from such over-the-top, exotic personal decoration. Miller's theory is that the beautiful tail developed over the eons because peahens liked them and favoured male peacocks with a wonderful display over dull, ordinary males with little or none. This is what Darwin described as 'sexual selection through mate choice'.

Sexual selection through mate choice

This is an important theory because, argues Miller, it doesn't only explain peacocks, or indeed any other kind of decoration or embellishment, be it appearance, humour or story-telling, etc. It also explains how and why the brain enlarged so massively, marking us out so definitively from other species.

'Before language evolved, our ancestors could not easily perceive one another's thoughts, but once language had arrived, thought itself became the subject of sexual selection' (Miller). Sexual selection may actually have been responsible for the development of language. He describes a positive self-feedback loop, driven by that most powerful of sensual urges. Sexual preference reinforces developing language, which in turn reinforces sexual preference. A human primate female constantly selects the male whose grunts and growls are most interesting to her, and over the centuries those grunts and growls refine into language.

HUMOUR IS SEXY

The male who displays the most versatile courtship is also likely to display the most health, intelligence and fitness – all evolutionary advantages. Humour, rated highly in today's psychological tests of desirable partner traits, would have evolved simultaneously, since humour would give an edge to ordinary speech. The humorous partner would have an advantage over the less-amusing partner.

Miller's theory is strenuously opposed by some scientists, most notably Steven and Hilary Rose. Their view is that the theory is too general and that there are too many assumptions to make it meaningful. Yet Miller makes an interesting point when he states that early hominids continued perfectly well for thousands of years *without* evolving this highly sophisticated brain. Brain size only tripled in our ancestors between two and a half million and a hundred thousand years ago. *If it were only natural selection that was driving us*, he believes, *we wouldn't have needed anything extra.*

More than one type of evolution
Natural selection accounts for our survival as hominids.
But it needs something else to explain that sudden leap in
brain size. Miller argues that sexual selection does this. He
writes, 'sexual selection through mate choice is a fickle,
unpredictable, diversifying process. It takes species that
make their livings in nearly identical ways and gives them
radically different sexual ornaments. It never happens the
same way twice. It drives divergent rather than convergent
evolution.' By this theory, it is sexual selection that
enlarges the brain in the first place and then accounts for
the subsequent development of creativity and imagination.
For it was only after the hundred-thousand year mark that
people began to grow civilised.

WOMEN SHAPE HISTORY?
SURELY NOT!
Another reason why the theory of sexual diversity
through mate selection may not have been taken
seriously is because it depends on conceding to
women the power to shape men – not the other way
round. Or at least it does when applied to animals.
With humans it seems highly likely that sexual selection is a two-way process.

Is there really a 'right' way to put a penis in a vagina?

So how does sexual selection theory affect the experience of penis in vagina today? Surely, evolved or otherwise, actual heterosexual intercourse always did consist of penis in vagina, give or take a few variations? We come back to a point made at the beginning of this chapter on sexual selection. Perhaps today's constraints about sex, all those 'beliefs' that there are right ways and wrong ways of doing it, all those orgasmic hurdles men and women feel forced to jump through, perhaps all of these are forms of evolutionary test. If you apply the sexual selection theory to our most intimate life, we could be weeding out the partners who are unsuited to the evolution of our line. If you feel uncomfortable and uneasy with one partner in bed, odds are there will be some discomfort and unease in other parts of the relationship. Would this be the person you want as parent to your children? Answer: probably not.

It's true that there aren't many guarantees that the partner who does inspire trust, and a good open sex life, will be a good long-term parent either. But at least his/her attractions get the chance to be passed on through his/her share of your child's genetic make-up.

Testing your partner with sex

So restraints on sex, even sex problems, might be evolutionary tests. If you get the answer to them right, i.e, if you manage to sort out the sex problem and overcome the communication difficulties, you pass the test. If you fail, that's it. Your joint line is doomed. It could be a powerful method of weeding out the wrong partners.

Sex is an immensely powerful drive. One of the fears that today's humans have about dropping some of their inhibitions or prohibitions about sex is that, without these restraining modern influences, they might go mad and turn into wild animals. Since by evolution's standards we are only in a second stage of development, there may be some real truth lying behind such a fear. Who is to say that, let off the leash, we won't become our wild instinctive ancestors, rather than our thinking contemporary selves?

Some primitive behaviour is good

We certainly see the instinctive side of our nature where aggression is concerned. Behaviour in a crowd, for example, often overrides normal inhibition so that we seem to act out of character. A football match or a pop concert are excellent examples. Yet not all such 'primitive' behaviour is 'bad'. Exuberance, enthusiasm, sexual expression, might be termed 'good'. The fact that these are expressed in ways not generally termed 'civilised' does not necessarily down-rate such qualities.

Most sex therapists would prefer to see a little more of the overriding exuberance of the cave when it comes to sex and a lot less of the restraining influences of so-called civilisation. Where primitive man might not have given a stuff about his partner's orgasm, he may have possessed enough staying power and intelligence to want to prolong the good sensations of love making. With this as a possible desire he may have kept going long enough and strong enough for his partner to climax. Naturally this is pure speculation. We can have absolutely no idea of how sex was for our ancient ancestors. What is certain is that if sexual selection by mate choice is responsible for the kind of sex we get today, we humans are not yet selecting mates for their ability to provoke exquisite and infallible sexual enjoyment!

Something old, something new
Our present enjoyment of what goes on in bed is stuck somewhere between the old and the new. Instead of getting on with what intercourse offers, we make a song and dance about it. Instead of moving on to a more satisfactory sexual mate, we often feel stuck with the present one. Instead of accepting that some men and women prefer multiple matings, we tell ourselves fiercely that possession of the other person is all.

Jealousy, a powerful instinctive feeling, tells us to hang on fiercely to what (or who) we consider our territory yet, at the same time, natural sexual desire tells us how nice it would be to make love to Brad Pitt, Alicia Silverstone, Ewan McGregor or all the female Corrs together. Instead of tearing each other's clothes off in the street and coupling at the time we most feel like it, we bottle up those feelings and take them home where only hours later we can do something with them, and then discover that – what bad luck! – the moment has passed.

It's worth bearing in mind that we are still in the process of evolution – we always will be. Hence the uncertainties, the need to feel secure when in actuality we can never be completely secure. These are some of the conflicts between our primitive side and our sophisticated one. And to make life even more interesting, 'sexual selection' is not the only theory that affects how we think about sex. There is another newer theory that allows us to see things from a different viewpoint.

As one meme said to another

One rare ability that humans share with only a very few other creatures is the ability to imitate. Other great apes, dolphins, certain whales, a few birds and rats can do this too and because they can, we rate them among the most highly intelligent species on this planet, second only to us.

When you imitate, something has been passed on. It may be an idea, a story, a type of behaviour, the way you move your arms when you are enthusiastic, no matter what … Whatever it is that has been imitated, it has now been given a name. It is called a 'meme'. Richard Dawkins, author of *The Selfish Gene*, first mentioned it in 1976 but the psychologist Susan Blackmore got to thinking about the idea of memes during a long recuperation from illness and the result was her fascinating book, *The Meme Machine*.

Her chapters on memes and sex are particularly pertinent. She begins by making a point that sex, power and food are evolutionarily powerful subjects and that one of the reasons we see so many books about sex (and food) is that we are still driven by these primitive drives. Our present day brains have evolved to focus specifically on such vital interests. In addition, anything that presses the sex button is also a meme: any stories, items of information, films, photographs. For what are these but methods of repeating, informing, replicating information?

A meme is a kind of ideas virus

But Blackmore goes much further when she theorises that all modern sexual behaviour is meme-driven. She sees a meme as a kind of ideas virus with a mission to survive, just as genetic material has a mission to survive. Many memes are passed from parent to child, such as how to eat cleanly, how to pass the butter. Children also get their first language from their parents and in so doing rely entirely on the power of imitation. What we have to get our head round here is that it is not only the information which is passed on, but also the meme. A successful meme is an idea which has survived in some form or other since the beginning of intelligent hominids.

CHINESE-WHISPER MEMES
Any information changes as it gets passed from one person to another. We've all played the game of Chinese whispers. The whispered information that arrives at the far end of the line is often very different from the information that started off.

There are three main methods of transferring memes, says Blackmore. First is 'vertical transmission' where information is passed on neatly from parent to child. Then there is 'horizontal transmission' which is between peers, for example the sort of sex information that we talked about earlier. The third is 'oblique transmission', such as that between uncle and nephew or from older to younger cousin.

The 'vertical' sex meme
The reason the type of transmission matters is because in the first (vertical) and to some extent the third (oblique), the ideas get handed on alongside the genetic material. In other words we will continue to learn and adapt, as our family always has for generation after generation.

If we apply this to sex, we might, for example, continue to believe that sex should only be confined to the partner we marry; that we shouldn't experience sex before the wedding; that sex should be done in the privacy of the marriage bed, probably at the weekends when we are not tired out; that sex is merely one of many aspects of family life. Because this is a lifestyle that has suited the family up until now there will be little conflict involved in doing sex this way.

Memes and marriage
Many of the memes which we are in the process of discarding are to do with ensuring the survival of the family line – keeping the family gene-pool pure. The idea of marriage, the horrible punishments for adultery, the notion that monogamy is better than other marriage practices contribute to these. This last meme is particularly interesting because it appears to be inaccurate.

> POLYANDRY IS GOOD FOR YOU!
> Blackmore writes of a group of people living in the high Himalayas who practise fraternal polyandry. One woman marries two or more brothers who inherit the family land. Studies of this group have shown that their system does, in fact, maximise their genetic fitness. Grandmothers with polyandrous daughters were found to have more surviving offspring than those with monogamous daughters. This system is founded upon the idea handed down from generation to generation (vertical) that survival is maximised by such an arrangement. Sadly however, the arrangement is now breaking down. As such remote villages come into contact with the rest

of civilisation ideas of work and marriage change. Such is the power of horizontal transmission.

What I think Susan Blackmore is speculating about, although she doesn't actually state it, is the possibility that the spreading of one's own ideas, to a point where you might even influence world view, may be a basic instinctive drive in itself. Some people, independently, are taking such notions very seriously indeed: the Gorbachov World Peace Forum, formed some eight years ago, meets every September to formulate ideas which it hopes to transmit into the ether, as an attempt to promote world peace. On the basis of the meme theory there is sound reasoning behind such a plan.

The 'horizontal' sex meme

When memes are transmitted horizontally, i.e. between school friends or colleagues at work, there is no guarantee that the ideas themselves will match the family ideas. So new notions are brought in which, although they may be exciting, will also be in conflict, both with family values and, perhaps, even with our own inner sense of what is safe and what isn't.

THE GROUP SEX MEME

A crude sexual example would be the young man from a traditional family who is invited to a group

sex party. He may want to take part and may get turned on by the excitement, but he may also feel out of his depth and be forced to get very drunk in order to cope. His new memes are in conflict with his old ones. And what will now be transmitted to the next generation – the new or the old? So the ideas themselves become embattled. Which meme will win?

Susan Blackmore feels that in modern society, where memes can be transmitted rapidly by the media or the internet, our way of life is transforming very fast indeed. The success of an idea today depends on its speedy transmission. In future, therefore, it will be the rapidly versatile who will do best, rather than the slow plodders.

The Mata Hari meme

So what are the connections between memes and the intimacy of sex? The intimacy of sex is such that it lends itself to the sharing of ideas. Beautiful female Mata Haris have traditionally used the bed as a method of extracting secret information. But perhaps more relevant to readers of this book is the connection between stories, ideas, and scenarios acted out as a prelude to the sex act. This type of sexual prelude may have come to us from peers rather than parents. We may not yet feel entirely comfortable with it but, almost certainly, sex games are here to stay.

Many of us are highly resistant to the idea of new sex practices, feeling swamped or out of our depth. This doesn't mean that we are not interested. Sex is a powerful trigger – most of us would love to learn more. One method of dealing with a meme too far would consist of inventing a meme of our own. If sex systems are up for grabs, if truly anything goes, the world would be able to cope with whatever we can come up with too. If politicians and philosophers can dream up new ideas, so too can you or I. We are just as entitled to float our own world view and ourdream of how it ought to be. We can feel confident about our own ideas instead of ashamed. Yet not everyone has thought this through. We need to take on board enough self-confidence to believe such a self-based thought. It is not other people who are the problem. *We* are the problem.

We invent our own sexual experience

Very few of us actually see other people doing sex. It isn't customary in the West to view parents' coupling. This means that we have no practical example to follow. From a meme point of view this means that our meme of doing sex is incomplete. When we actually get down to fucking, we operate from having heard about the act, perhaps having seen pictures and, occasionally, films, but never having experienced the feelings involved. We bring to early sexual experience therefore a combination of incomplete ideas

plus instinct. How we actually relate to A N Other therefore, how intimate we manage to become, is *one of the few
things we make up for ourselves.*

We invent our sexual experience, based on theories fed
into us by parents and culture. Some of us manage it with
artistry, some with enough ease for pleasurable enjoyment
and some of us make a balls-up. I come back therefore to
the thought that since we actually invent part of our sexual
experience we can reinvent it too. Or we can build on the
invention, extending its parameters. It is *our* experience,
not someone else's. And therefore, *if we want to change it
we can.*

New brain research

Current research and thinking about the brain also offers
up-to-date ideas about how to handle life. Through further understanding of how the human brain works we
are getting a new handle on how to think about sex.
Neuro-scientists believe that the left hemisphere of the
brain contains an area that has been dubbed the 'interpreter'. The right brain is a kind of automatic brain,
which lets us respond to stimuli in what feels like an
instinctive manner. The instincts may have come from the
evolutionary years prior to consciousness when we reacted
automatically to certain stimuli.

The interpreter in the left brain allows us to build on
strong bursts of neuronal activity, such as pleasure or pain.

most people settle
on the missionary

This can increase the build-up to become a belief that, for example, the missionary position is one of the most pleasurable ways of experiencing sex.

How we get stuck in the missionary position

Factors taken in and unconsciously weighed by the interpreter in the left brain will be: the intimacy of full-frontal sexuality; the easy access to each other's pleasure zones, especially to the clitoris; the proximity of the sensually laden lips to those of your mate. In the early months of the relationship the missionary position will get honed to perfection so that it delivers the goods in the most satisfactory manner possible.

Next, the missionary sex routine crosses over from the left brain, where it has been constructed and 'interpreted', to the right brain, where your way of having sex is now stored as a 'given'. From now on, the way you do sex will be virtually automatic. You will unconsciously go, most often, to doing sex in the missionary position. It has become instinctive. It has been established in your right brain pathways as *your* sex pattern. (For further details about this system of experiencing then storing, see Susan Greenfield's *The Human Brain – a Guided Tour*.)

On reading this you may feel indignant. 'Of course I have sex in a variety of patterns,' you may think with irritation. 'There is no one way in which I experience sex.

I am a thinking, conscious human being with choices in this life.'

Brain science would have us think that *all* choices are limited by the premise that any thoughts and beliefs we hold are founded upon the very first primitive firing of neurones. We're talking about those sparks of brain activity our ancient ancestors experienced when they coupled with the entire tribe or even when they masturbated as they sat high up in a tree. Most people hate this analogy, rejecting it fiercely. But if you try the experiment of allowing yourself to contemplate it, it can be helpful. Deep down there is an animal inside us, albeit an extremely bright one. Why should it hurt to get in touch with that animal? The civilised newer layer of the brain is not going to allow you to run amok.

How sex in the brain works

It might feel safer to get in touch with the 'animal inside' if you knew a little more about the way in which the sex centres of the brain work. An incredibly simplified description would be to say that the little grey cells transmit chemical messengers called hormones to other cells. Each hormone transmits a different message. If you see someone who turns you on, your brain sends out chemicals that get you into sexual mode, so that you lubricate and get a mini-erection of the clitoris if you are female or gain a penile erection if you are male.

But unfortunately for our understanding of it the brain then gets much trickier. Sex researchers at the Kinsey Institute are beginning to believe that the brain contains at least two centres, possibly three, that balance sex feelings. The first centre is an 'excitor', an area that pretty obviously gives rise to sexual excitement, i.e. arousal. The second centre is an 'inhibitor', an area that clamps down on feelings of sexual excitement and prevents arousal. The two work in combination to provide a balanced sexual behaviour. The inhibitor prevents you from becoming overtly sexy in inappropriate surroundings. The third is also an 'inhibitor', though scientists are not yet so sure about this one. They reckon it might explain why some people experience a kind of global shut-down of sexual feelings.

Balancing excitement and inhibition

However, the ratio of excitement to inhibition can go wrong. President Clinton is an example of a man who suffers from too much excitement and not enough inhibition. This means that, from time to time, he behaves sexually in a way that is unacceptable to American society. It is highly likely that it is his sexual brain centres that are directing this behaviour rather than his conscious choice.

OVER-CONTROLLING INHIBITION

Another problem that might be caused by this imbalance between excitement and inhibition is that

of the widower who can't make love to his new partner because he feels he is being unfaithful to his late
wife. His emotions cause his inhibition.

Then there is the mother who can't relax in bed
because she fears her toddler will wander into the
bedroom. She clearly has a concrete reason for feeling inhibited.

Some of the women in my sexuality therapy groups found
it so difficult to turn on that they couldn't climax with their
partner even though they wanted to. These women probably suffered from an overactive dose of inhibition. But we
proved in the group that if you work on overcoming the
inhibition, sexual desire really does get a chance to gleam
through. In the 1970s and 1980s we used therapeutic
methods that involved gaining trust, reading sexually stimulating material, even watching sexy films. Today, there are
pills that work much faster to regulate these two centres.

PILLS AND THERAPY

VIAGRA helps men get erections, though it may not
give them desire.

PHENTOLAMINE can lower inhibition. Neither of these
drugs is suitable for everyone though.

BETA-BLOCKERS lower anxiety levels and slow sexual
response.

SEX THERAPY can work at raising levels of sexual

excitement and lowering anxiety so that inhibition doesn't cut in so fast as it did with the women in my sexuality groups.

General mood also affects sexual response. Anxiety, fear, anger, and depression play their part but since the next chapter focuses on how preconceived ideas affect our sexual receptivity, mood will be fully described there.

Different systems – different views

We are in the middle of a major upheaval in our sexual thinking. If the theory of memes is correct, memes have spread to a point where they are truly breaking down established patterns while other sex patterns are being bandied about. This can be both exciting and scary. How can we know how to judge anything? What will constitute a good sexual relationship? Does any of this matter anyway? After all, however you choose to think about it, heterosexual sex continues to consist of putting penis into vagina. Doesn't it?

THE MOON GOES INTO THERAPY

Did you hear the story about the moon going around the earth? The moon discovered psychotherapy. It went in for long and intensive counselling sessions. When it finally emerged, it did, it explained, feel quite different. Whereas previously it had revolved thoughtlessly around and around the earth, now, the moon disclosed proudly, it chose to do so.

Unique experiences

The moon story is a parable for our times. And is, obviously, intended as a joke. Yet there is a chunk of the story that remains important. We are the only people who can have our experience. No one else can do it for us. We encounter external events in a way specific to ourselves, which affects how we ultimately live our lives because such experiences alter our brain make-up. If we have been savagely raped as a young teenager, we are not going to feel the same about subsequent sex as the young man or woman who chooses the exact time and circumstances in which to enjoy safe, pleasurable sensuality for their first time. Mental attitudes to sex are changed by external events. But mental attitudes can be improved.

Change through extreme pleasure

Change does not only have to come from the external or from the unpleasant. We can change:

- through gaining knowledge;
- by deliberately putting ourselves in the path of certain memes;
- thanks to extreme pleasure – a fact not often noted by psychotherapists although this constitutes the main

working premise for sex therapists;
- by taking seriously old ideas from former times instead of discarding them on the grounds that old means out of date;
- by taking on new ideas that offer us new perspectives;
- by daring to open ourselves up to experience that would not be a traditional choice.

Who is to say, for example, that the swingers of the 1970s experienced poor-quality sexuality? Can we learn anything from swingers? Many people would say, 'certainly not', but they cannot know. They cannot be in the brains of those people. When swingers say that they gain a power-fully effective eroticism, a vital sense of freedom, an actual orgasmic experience that is multiplied in strength, they could be absolutely right. No one else can experience their feeling. So no one else can know if they have discovered some kind of sensuality that has escaped the rest of us.

All very well, you might argue, but swingers possess the temperament that allows them to cope with swinging. If you don't have the temperament, you won't have posi-tive experiences. True again, but temperament isn't every-thing. Opening up to experiment is part of the picture. Please understand, I am not making a compelling argu-ment for the whole world to start swinging. (I'd go to the barricades to protest against *any* enforced sexual beliefs.) But I am attempting to explain that a different mind-set leads to different experiences – even if ultimately they are based on continuing to revolve around the earth.

In order to open yourself up to anything different, new or potentially threatening, it is necessary to rid yourself of preconceived fears and prejudices. Chapter 2 offers some thoughtful exercises on how to go about doing that.

Moods and emotions

Strong feelings

Moods and emotions play a big part in the experience of sex. This sounds so obvious that you probably wonder why I even bother stating it. The reason lies in new information about the brain. There is now a strong suspicion that the areas of the brain that deal with strong emotion may be situated next door to areas that deal with sex. It seems highly likely that one 'little grey cell' can seep its intelligence into and over to the adjacent ones.

So this means that if, for example, you are deeply depressed, your sex centres get depressed too, thus making it difficult to get turned on. If you are prone to deep-seated anxiety, your sex drive may get anxious too and need to be reassured over and over again by the sex act itself. Most people probably think that if an individual is anxious, the sex act itself would become fraught with anxiety and suffer. But surprisingly, sexological studies have proved virtually the opposite.

Anxiety

Professor John Bancroft, author of *Human Sexuality and its Problems*, studied men who were told they would be given an electric shock if they produced an erection. You might expect such unfortunates to become extremely anxious and to respond by wilting in all directions. But no! Eight out of the ten men studied showed that it made no difference to their state of erection and two found that it actually enhanced erection. One of these explained that since his early teens he would get slight erections when feeling anxious.

> SEX AND PRESIDENTS
>
> Another theory about President Clinton is that he is a man who associates feeling better with sexual release. When you think about the major stresses he has had to juggle daily, his behaviour, unsuitable though it is for a president, does not seem so surprising. His situation can be seen as an illustration of how muddled the states of anxiety and sexuality can become!

It's those muddled states of anxiety and sexuality that are worth concentrating on. Because if ever there were an example of how reactions can run riot it is in the range of responses that human beings experience sexually as a result of anxiety. According to Bancroft anxiety can:

- interfere with sexual response, either speeding it up or slowing it down;
- interfere with thought processes that would lead to a reasoned assessment of the situation;
- be avoided by inhibiting some sexual responses;
- be a reaction to sexual failure;
- facilitate sexual response.

I don't list these possibilities to confuse you, though you could be forgiven if they do, but to illustrate how different our various responses can be to the same emotion. Individuals, possessing different ideas about life, will feel these enormously varied responses.

Anger

There is also evidence that anger can sometimes fuel and facilitate sexual response rather than inhibit it. One fascinating story from my women's therapy groups of the 1970s concerned Clare. Clare had never climaxed and was ignorant about how her sexual response worked. The day she took her newly acquired vibrator home was a day when she was in an extremely bad temper. She unpacked the vibrator in the bathroom and, in a fit of rage, decided it couldn't possibly work and jammed it between her legs to prove it. She climaxed almost immediately and fell into the bath with shock. Rage had speeded up the process for her.

Moral of this story: don't automatically assume that

powerful negative emotions mean you can't be sexual. Adjust your ideas and find out.

Anger affects sex in several interesting ways:

- As Clare found, it may *improve* sexual response.
- Some people cannot feel both angry and sexy at the same time. Perhaps a degree of anger is stimulating, but if it increases and resentment evolves, then this further degree of rage erodes sex.
- Avoidance or rejection of sexual activity may be a way of expressing anger.
- Rape is a vicious method of expressing anger.

E l a t i o n

Depression and elation are at opposite ends of the emotional spectrum and each can influence what goes on between the sheets. Gina suffered from bi-polar disorder, the condition that used to be called manic depression. On the occasions when she felt manic she felt sexually empowered. Her drive was high, her energy boundless, and her confidence endless. With these as a basis of physical and emotional well-being she believed she could do virtually anything sexual. And did – no holds barred. She swung. She enjoyed multiple partners. She climaxed easily and quickly. She believed she was powerfully attractive and acted as if she were. Men flocked around her.

You may get the impression from this that Gina was a young, beautiful woman with a perfect shape – the kind of

ideal we are told men really go for. It could come as a surprise to learn that Gina was overweight, middle-aged and
not particularly stylish. Which is my point. *You are as attractive as you feel you are. You can be almost anything you
want if you believe strongly. You are what you believe.*

Depression
As the disorder gained ground, Gina experienced depression more often than elation. With depression, everything
shut down. Her energy disappeared, her sex drive shrank,
her self-belief vanished. Instead of getting out and chasing
lovers, she could hardly stir from her room.

Gina's story is an extreme one. I recount it to provide
a dramatic illustration of how mood can affect both sexuality and self-belief. It is a curse to suffer from intense
mood swings. Nobody would wish it. But many of us
might want to gain some of the self-belief Gina experienced when manic. An important point about her story is
the fact that *her body chemistry affected her personal
beliefs.* The medical profession today is concentrating hard
on that connection between mind and body, not only for
sufferers from bi-polar disorder but for all the rest of us
who at some time or other fall prey to depression.

How depression affects sex drive
Depression
• lowers sexual desire;

- impairs erection in men;
- impairs erection and lubrication in women;
- makes orgasm difficult to reach.

Impaired sleep erections in men, which are found in cases of low sexual desire and low free-ranging testosterone, are also found in cases of depressive illness. New anti-depressants are constantly being developed to combat various forms of depression. These raise the mood and usually allow sexual desire and arousal to return.

> HORMONES AND SEX DRIVE
> It is now widely suspected that testosterone is responsible for sex drive in women as well as in men. So if depression hits men in the libido, there's every reason to think it will do the same for women. We also know that oestrogen is responsible for a general sense of well-being.

Mood treatments

When we get really depressed many of us feel desperate enough to opt for anti-depressants or talking treatments or, ideally, a combination of both. But one problem is that often *we don't recognise we have become depressed.*

We assume that feeling continually grim is normal. It isn't. To improve this kind of misery we need to do two things. The first is to halt the chemical aspect of depression in its tracks. This usually needs to be done first because without putting a brake on the depression, it is hard to concentrate on any kind of talking treatment. And when it is hard to concentrate it is very hard indeed to do any of the work needed to sort out our heads. Once the head feels clearer, thanks to anti-depressants, we get fit enough to tackle whatever caused the difficulty in the first place.

Moral of this story is: if your sex life has flown out of the window, stop and think about your mood. If you are depressed you may need an anti-depressant to stop the flow of misery and let you feel generally better. If you have any kind of hormone impairment, first of all you need to find out what your body chemicals are doing. When you have done so (by paying a visit to the doctor), you then need to think about hormone readjustment or, in cases of older men and women, hormone replacement.

Taking drugs? Aagh!!!

What? Take drugs? Without being ill? A terrible idea, I hear you cry. Stop for a minute and think. Please. 'An idea', that's what you automatically said. If we go back to the theory of memes, an idea is something that can mutate. Why should your idea that taking drugs is harmful still hold true today? Wouldn't it be worth reassessing the situation at least? Drugs have traditionally been held to be a bad idea because they might be addictive and/or possess dangerous side-effects.

These beliefs were based on an historic reality. Early development of drugs has been a hazardous process. But we have been developing them now for well over a century. Many of the prejudices we feel today were sensible 20 years ago. But things move fast in biochemical research and before we dismiss an important life choice out of hand we ought at least to get ourselves up to scratch.

Drugs as lifesavers

These days we don't hesitate to turn to drugs when we feel that there is just cause to use one. We hail them as life savers when we:

- recover from cancer;
- don't die from gangrene;
- mitigate the ravages of arthritis;
- survive common flu instead of dying from the high temperatures it engenders.

We still believe we should not resort to drugs without dire cause. So far it is only life-saving situations or intense pain that allow us to feel drug-taking is OK. Yet now that drugs that affect well-being are becoming honed and statistically safe, couldn't we begin to change our beliefs a tad?

Why should we have to feel seriously ill before we can improve the quality of life? One of the golden rules of assertion training is that it is all right to change your mind because doing so is a sign of maturity.

Drugs that improve sex

Drugs can now:

- improve our body chemistry so that we no longer experience depression and as a result experience the rejuvenation of sexual desire;
- moderate both the excitor and the inhibitor centres in the brain so that we can turn on or turn off when previously this has been difficult;
- prolong and assist erection;
- dampen down anxiety so that we can function well enough to improve our relationship with the man or woman we love and subsequently our performance in the bedroom.

One reason why it's important to keep your mind open is because new information is constantly being fed into it. A computer shifts its conclusions slightly every time new data is entered – so too do our brains. If you add a couple of new facts to the hotchpotch of beliefs presently jostling for space, you gain a new picture.

Drugs are moving into a second phase

There is also a powerful belief (another meme) that the forthcoming century will see a greater acceptance of the miracle drugs which prevent emotional suffering, much as chemotherapy and penicillin eased physical suffering in the last. For drugs have moved into a second phase. Now that we know we can cure or at least halt the progression of serious illness, the next step is not only to deal with life or death situations but to look at the *quality of life* as well.

We only have one life to live. And it is a short one. If you knew that you were going to spend two thirds of it crippled with arthritis, wouldn't you gladly opt for a drug that would guarantee you pain-free flexible joints, even if you did have to take one of those pills every day for the rest of your life? Why shouldn't we adopt the same attitude towards substances that improve the way we experience our sex life?

We don't mind 'natural' cures, do we?

Men and women flock to 'natural' cures in their thousands. Healthfood shops sell tons of natural supplements, vitamins and creams. Aromatherapy has become big business with major chain stores selling aromatic oils. One out of four people reading this book is likely to have experienced some kind of massage using aromatic oil (or even baby oil). And lived to tell the tale. Did you know that those 'natural cures' still bring about physical and chemical changes, just as aspirin does? Most of us have been subjecting our bodies to these 'natural' chemical changes for years now and continue to function fine.

Men and women want to be sexy for ever

There is a lot of evidence to show that men and women,

given half a chance, are happy to be sexy for ever. Sixty-year-old women these days still only look around 40, compared to previous generations. That's thanks to hormone replacement. And far from risking your life through under-taking HRT, the opposite is probably true. You are likely to prolong it. Barbara Cartland, who died shortly before her 100th birthday, took oestrogen for more than half of her life.

> OESTROGEN EQUALS WELL-BEING
> Oestrogen makes you feel well. It also guards against osteoporosis and heart disease – two killers in old age. The evidence for oestrogen causing cancer continues to be debatable with studies showing both positive and negative results. If you are taking oestrogen though, you are more likely to receive regular gynaecological check-ups so that if there are any pre-cancerous changes they will be spotted early and dealt with, giving a good chance of healthy life for years after.

Pass the sex gel

Testosterone, which has been regarded with suspicion for 50 years, has finally come of age. Research shows that regular testosterone use for men over a period of almost 50 years, far from causing health problems, safeguards against arteriosclerosis and allows men to feel energetic, ·

good tempered and reassuringly sexual. There is no equivalent long-term information about women yet, but individual reports of women using testosterone gel rubbed into
the skin, indicate that these women feel stronger, have
more energy, enjoy increased sexual sensation in the genitals and achieve orgasm with greater ease. Unless some
totally unexpected finding (which hasn't happened with
men) demonstrates a disastrous side-effect, can you think
of any reason why women should not feel all these life-
affirming sensations for as long as is possible? I can't.

Why am I bothering to bang on this way if you are
prejudiced against taking drugs? Because I hope to start
you thinking differently about them. I hope that, through
the information presented here, fresh ideas will allow you
to process the pill-gulping decision with more real choice.
If you block out information because of prejudice, you do
not possess real choice. I can't bear important options to
be missed because your decisions are based on out-dated
facts from 50 years ago.

So what about those beliefs (or prejudices) that we
started off with? Let's go over them.

Addiction

Yes, we may find we can't manage very well without the
drugs, once we've started. But this isn't surprising since we
weren't managing very well before we started taking them.
In fact, that is *why* we started taking them. What the drugs

increasingly do is fulfil a function that our body, for reasons of its own, has stopped doing. I suspect most of us wouldn't think twice about using a bionic leg aid, if our real leg could hardly function – given the opportunity of receiving a leg aid that looked exactly like the real one. And if the real leg eventually chose not to walk at all, well, there would be no argument, would there? We would be grateful for the bionic system and might even find that certain walking and running abilities functioned better than the original. Drugs go one better. With drugs there is the possibility that their use may kick-start the original system into functioning again so that we don't have to prolong their use.

In the past we have only considered using drugs as a temporary measure to get us better. In the future we may choose to use drugs long-term to improve our quality of life. The fact that thousands of men opted for Viagra when it first hit the market shows we are already moving in this direction. And if women thought that a female version of this little blue pill would guarantee them a good sexual response (including an orgasm) it is highly likely that women too would start popping pills with far greater ease. Some psychiatrists already believe that long-term usage of certain medications would improve the quality of life for great swathes of the population.

Dangerous side-effects

If you heard that a particular pill would make you turn blue, then, if you were sensible, you would research it before rejecting it out of hand. If you subsequently discovered that it is only people with blood group B-positive who turn blue, and you know you are not B-positive then, on the face of it, there wouldn't seem to be much reason for holding back from improving your life.

You need to know as much as possible about all side-effects of any pill before swallowing it. But you can only make a responsible decision when all the facts are marshalled before you. So one duty of anyone wanting to improve their love life chemically is to thoroughly research the consequences of their choice first. But if, on having done so, the evidence is that you will be able to tolerate the drug, please don't then dismiss it out of prejudice.

Sex hormones through the skin

Many of the new sex substances used in hormone replacement are now formulated as gels or creams to be rubbed into the skin rather than taken by mouth. The great advantage of this method is that the substance gets directly into the blood stream without having to be processed by the stomach and liver. Much of the damage done to the human system through pill swallowing is a result of damage to the liver. Now we know to avoid this method.

So before dismissing the notion of drug-taking out of

hand please research the substance in question. Read the accompanying notes that arrive with it. Look it up in medical dictionaries, go to the internet and feed details of the drug into as many search engines as you can muster. If what you get back is a catalogue of disasters, don't go near it. But if the reviews are favourable, please consider it. Especially if it comes in gel or cream form.

A sex programme for change

Clinical proof of mind over matter

'An erection cannot be willed' – this is a common belief and, on the face of it, one that appears to be true. Men usually can't produce erections for every circumstance. Or at least we believe this to be the case, but this is only partly true. The evidence shows something else. Surveys, clinical studies, and laboratory experiments have demonstrated that many men and women can produce genital responses at will, by thinking sexual thoughts or unrolling sexual fantasies in their heads. And they can do this in front of other people, for example in front of laboratory technicians. The same experiments have also shown that people can distract themselves from becoming turned on by thinking non-sexual thoughts.

The use of erotic films and of fantasy fired up the sexual systems of these men and women under observation, resulting in all kinds of delicious sensory reactions in circumstances where most of us would have thought that feeling sexy was a non-starter. •

Your malfunctioning sex life is your choice

On the strength of this information, let me float an idea: unless there is something physically wrong – a possibility that can be established by medical tests – *you will be able to function sexually*. The only reason you won't be functioning sexually therefore is because you don't want to. In other words, even if you are not consciously doing this, you are unconsciously choosing not to be sexual. Your lack of desire or erection might feel like a problem. It certainly may be creating a problem. *But it is your choice.*

In this event you might like to think about your need for making this choice. What is such a choice letting you do that in other circumstances you couldn't or wouldn't? What benefits/advantages does it bring?

Alternatively you might like to change that choice now that you realise you have made it. Or you might like to think about changing your relationship. How you make such decisions depends on the ideas you bring to the problem situation and the ways in which you choose to reframe them.

So let's contemplate reframing. In therapeutic circles this is called 'cognitive feedback'.

Sexual attitude restructuring

No, I didn't make this phrase up. Sexual attitude restructuring (SAR) is an idea pioneered by the Reverend Ted

McIlvenna of the Glide Foundation and of the Institute for the Advanced Study of Human Sexuality in San Francisco. It is a process that mature students (willingly) undergo before studying for their qualifications in human sexuality. The institute is the only organisation in the US licensed to award a degree in human sexuality and has been for the past 25 years.

In order to approach the subject of human sexuality with a non-judgemental approach, institute officials (these include Wardell Pomeroy, one of the co-authors of the famous Kinsey report) realised that contemporary men and women are thoroughly handicapped by the sex information they have already picked up in the world and therefore need retraining. How could an individual expect to make important decisions about sex, if s/he is filled with prejudice and misbelief?

At the very least SAR training aims to provide up-to-date, accurate information about human sexual behaviour. At the most, it hopes to clear the mind of misinformation and prejudice so that the students can go on to make balanced and reasonable decisions about their own sex lives and about men and women who are likely to be their counselling clients. Most SAR students are already in the helping professions while others are just beginning their training. Students are typically sex therapists, counsellors, social workers, teachers, psychiatrists, psychologists, and family doctors.

A blitz of sex films

The SAR weekend consists of a blitz of sex-education films interspersed by discussion on the particular sexual subject that has been featured. Over the weekend the students view around 60 separate films; these are often screened three at a time. The films are on almost every aspect of sexuality you might care to name. And they are not movies acted out by actors and actresses. They are films of real people – documentary style – showing their real sex patterns, the real ways in which they actually make love, have sex, fuck.

Glide Foundation films

In 1964, Ted McIlvenna, a young Methodist minister, came to the Methodist Glide Foundation to work with young people. While doing so he became acutely aware of how alienated young homosexuals were from the church and of how damaged they became when they did try to seek advice from clergy, physicians or others, often because of the personal hang-ups of these so-called 'helpers'. Realising that you can't understand homosexuality without understanding human sexuality, McIlvenna and his team began experimenting with a new and exceedingly controversial system to help professionals gain a broader view of sex so that, in turn, they could truly help people in distress.

He and Laird Sutton, a young film maker, asked per-

mission of certain men and women – couples, often students – to film them making love. When the films were
edited the 'actors' were promised that the resulting movies
would be shown to them first so that they could comment
on whether or not they felt the footage to be a fair por-
trayal of their sexual behaviour. If the films were considered inaccurate the couple could and did have the power
of veto.

Over the years the Glide Foundation built up a bank of
sex films unlike any other, virtually constituting a thesis in
themselves. Here, on the screen, could be seen a unique
archive of real sexual behaviour.

It sounds easy described on paper, almost 40 years
after the inception of such an extraordinary project. But
making such films while maintaining any kind of dignified
and respected status quo was not easy. It says a great deal
for Ted McIlvenna's giant personality that he managed to
make it look effortless when it can have been nothing of
the sort. His was a truly original and innovative inspira-
tion. The films and the ensuing discussion became the basis
for the training scheme, which 11 years later became the
foundation of the institute.

After the ball is over
By the time a SAR weekend is over everyone attending can
talk about any aspect of sex without turning a hair. This
means that it provides wonderful food for mending your

own relationship. It also means that when a client comes to you, finding it exceedingly hard to talk about a subject so traditionally secret, they respond to *your* comfort with the subject. They grow comfortable themselves. How many people do you know who have tried to talk about sexual difficulties with a doctor or counsellor only to come to an abrupt halt because the helper in question is so embarrassed by the subject?

You might expect that some participants of such an overt training system would be dissatisfied with the extraordinarily intimate nature of the subject matter. Sensibly, McIlvenna and his staff have been careful to take notice of all feedback. Statistics show that 96 per cent of participants find the SAR very helpful both personally and professionally. Three per cent are not sure and 1 per cent find it of no value. I doubt if many other training establishments could show such remarkable results.

If Ted McIlvenna himself had not been able to shed traditional thoughts and prejudices about sex, his extraordinary training institution would never have produced the thousands of graduates that it has done over the years. Almost all sex educators in the US and Canada and many more in the UK have experienced the SAR programme – not only the weekend course specifically referred to here but the full-time training that results in several different types of degree award.

Turning your own sex life around

For a long time we have been aware that persons attending the Forum's basic introductory course have in great measure *solved a lot of their sexual problems*. This has also been observed by others in the sex field. Our conclusion is that most of so-called sexual dysfunction results from lack of knowledge. Where there is no physical problem involved most persons find they can change their patterns simply through a *change of attitude and actions* whether or not they have had difficulty in achieving orgasm, controlling premature ejaculation or maintaining potency. [My emphasis.]

SAR *Guide* (1975).

I am going to outline a few exercises based on SAR methods in the hope that they will allow you to develop a familiarity with sex so that it is not so loaded a subject. I do this in the hope that once sex stops being quite such a big deal you too will find you are able to think differently about it and to make decisions about sex in a less stressed manner. Naturally, I can only outline here a few of the ideas that the institute teaches in great detail. What you see in these pages is entirely my own version of attitude restructuring: if you want to enrol for the real thing you will find the address and telephone number of the institute in the appendix.

I also hope I've made a good enough case in the two preceding chapters for offering here a system that allows

you to look at sex differently via a process of getting familiar with deeply intimate sex acts.

How to change your sexual prejudices – a programme

If you want to get the most out of this programme I suggest you work through it sequentially. You need to read straight through the entire collection of visualisations that follows, stopping only briefly in between visualisations to think through your feelings or, if you are with a friend or in a group, to talk through thoroughly what you have read. If you break off halfway through the series and come back to it later you won't get the same impact and the programme won't work. The object of the programme is to get much more comfortable with sexual intimacy until you reach a point where you can accept a variety of sex acts without bringing judgemental attitudes to them. You don't have to change one iota regarding your own sex life if you don't want to. Nothing is imperative. But it would be good to think that you might change your acceptance of others.

Know yourself

In order to change your sexual attitudes, you need to know first what they consist of. These questions allow you to take yourself through a type of sex life history. Please answer the questions sequentially.

1   What ideas about sex did you gain from your parents?

2   What kind of a loving or non-loving example did your parents set?

3   If you could take a guess at the quality of your parents' sex life, how would you rate it? Excellent, good, fair, poor, non-existent?

4   Who or what else did you learn about sex from? Siblings, school friends, other friends, teachers, magazines?

5   At what age did you discover masturbation? And in what circumstances? How did you feel about it?

6   Have you ever fantasised? And if you have, how old were you when this first happened?

7   Did you ever experience sex (wet) dreams as a child?

8   Do your religious beliefs play any part in your experience of sexuality?

9   How important is sexual pleasure to you?

10 Have you experienced orgasm?

11 Do you feel comfortable in talking about sex?

12 How old were you when you had your first sex experience?

13 Did this feel good or poor?

14 In what physical circumstances did you first have sex, for example bed, car, field?

15 What has been your best sex experience?

16 What has been your worst sex experience?

17 How many sex partners have you had during your
    lifetime?
18 Have you taken part in any group sex activity, for
    example threesome, couples, swinging, etc?
19 Have you ever been raped or forced into having sex
    against your will?
20 How do you feel about sex right now?
21 Have you had sexual relationzships outside your
    main relationship?
22 How do you feel about these?
23 What have you learned sexually from your long-term
    relationship(s)?

*The idea behind the questions is not that there are any right
or wrong answers but that by replying truthfully you may
get to know yourself rather better than before. Even though
we experience certain sexual events we don't always put
them together and make any kind of pattern from them. The
answers here will help you gain insight into your own particular sexual preferences.*

Patterns that can emerge are:
• an open enjoyment of sexuality – usually where the
   parental example has been a positive one and where
   discussion about sex in the family has been open;
• a difficulty in sexual enjoyment – often where the
   parental example has been negative, and sex a taboo

subject in the family. Very strong religious beliefs can also adversely affect sexual enjoyment;
- a difficulty in relating sexually to one particular person but not to others;
- a lack of relating sexually;
- an abundance of relating sexually that may get you into trouble.

What pattern can you see for yourself?

Know your partner
It's sensible to ask your partner to answer these questions too and then to share the results. If you are in the early days of your relationship, this probably won't be difficult. If you have been together for a while, it may get more sensitive. If you don't want to know about possible infidelities, leave out this section. By sharing information you can compare and pinpoint areas which you have in common and areas where you seem different. As a general rule, it makes sense to build on the shared aspects and work on opening up to the different ones.

What do you want to achieve from your sex life?
You probably wouldn't be reading this book if there wasn't something you specially wanted from it – even if it is simply to wallow in sexual ideas. Do you want to:
- know yourself better;

- widen your sexual horizons;
- improve your sexual expertise;
- feel sexy more of the time;
- improve the sexual side of your relationship;
- feel all right about doing something sexually daring?

What do you want? Try to get a handle on what you might be looking for at this particular moment in time.

Writing

Even if you can't write for toffee, try keeping a sexual diary. Nobody is going to read it except you. The value of this is that when you look back over a couple of months you will see patterns emerge in your sex life. Sometimes those patterns contradict what you have previously believed about yourself. One man had considered himself to be sexually inadequate, in part because he was constantly undermined by his father, but on rereading his diary he discovered himself to be highly sexual. He both satisfied his girlfriend and himself with intercourse and on the evenings he didn't see her, he always masturbated to orgasm. There was nothing wrong with his sex drive or his expression of it. But it took the proof, in black and white, to change his idea about himself.

Reading

Reading books about sex, and this includes sexy books,

fulfils several vital functions. You may:

- get to feel much hornier from reading about sex which, if you worry about not turning on easily, can be vastly reassuring;
- give yourself a rich sex life through books when your actual sex life feels presently empty;
- learn a lot about both sex and relationships – never a bad thing.

So please pay no attention to the critics who rubbish sexual reading material. If you want to read it, go right ahead. One safeguard here: if you are in a relationship where the other person may feel threatened by your reading sex books, please either explain that you are doing this as part of an educational course and invite them to join you; or, if you truly feel this wouldn't work, protect them by ensuring they don't know much about your reading matter.

Note: any time you meet with opposition to something that concerns sex, remind yourself that this opposition is based on one particular set of ideas. And that the reason you are clashing is because *you* hold a different set of ideas. You are entitled to hold your different ideas – and so are they. This is not a licence to upset or hurt others but it is a permission to feel all right about yourself. Just remind yourself you are experiencing a struggle between memes!

R u d e   w o r d s

Picture your favourite movie star. S/he is facing the camera holding a long list. It's so long that it looks like a reel of lavatory paper. This is a list of sex words, the star announces. S/he is going to read them out loud. And read them out loud s/he does. Here's the list:

fuck
cunt
wank
poke
arse
cum
prick
pull
lick
suck
thrust
rim
bitch
whore
gasp
groan
sweat
seep
drip
balls
testicles

> *finger fuck*
> *arse fuck*
> *screw*
> *jerk off*
> *dribble*
> *spill*
> *slip*
> *squirt*

Now read them aloud yourself – in a loud voice. Now do it again.

> *How are you feeling? Stopped in your tracks? Faintly shocked? Stimulated? Turned on? Carry on reading the list over and over again. Eventually you will find that the words carry less impact. Carry on some more. Eventually the words become simply ... words.*

Sexual practice

> *One way of finding out what your prejudices consist of is to embark on a series of daring visualisations. As you embark on each of the following visualisations, ask yourself how you feel about that particular scene. Do you experience violent loathing; dislike; nothing much; a pleasing tinge of interest; acute turn-on? Each of these reactions gives you a good idea of what you do or don't feel comfortable with. This process will help you to pinpoint your prejudices.*

Now we move on to a series of explicit sexual visualisations. Read them through quickly. When you finish, stop and examine your feelings.

Cute cartoon hamsters

Hammy and Honey are cute hamsters. They are young-sters, jumping about in the garden, enjoying the rough and tumble of childish games. They box, and scrabble and roll around, ending up as far away as the long grass. They possess very silly faces that register surprise every time they fetch up against a rock, a plant or each other. As they jump up and down on top of each other, their weight (hamsters are hefty little creatures) fair knocks the breath out of the other. You'd think they'd get used to this but no, every time it happens they look really puzzled. You can't help laughing. Every jump gets a bit more silly, with the creatures landing on each other in a variety of very silly positions, sideways, lengthways, upside down, sprawled across each other so that every position gets funnier. When the hamsters start jumping a bit more rhythmically and they (and you) realise that by sheer accident they are having sex the surprise on their faces is priceless. You all roar with laughter. The transition from fun to sex has been seamless. The hamsters are innocent and the sex is a part of playing.

You have just watched sex on the screen of your imagination. How do you feel? Try going over the scene again.

Young lovers

Switch your mind to a pair of young lovers. These are real lovers – not actors – an ordinary girl and boy, probably students at college. They are lying on his bed in the middle of the afternoon. You know this is real because the room is a mess and they haven't cleared up the dishes from lunchtime. They are fully clothed and kissing passionately. You can tell this isn't the first time they have made love because they look comfortable with each other. They are lying close, running their hands all over each other and delving underneath their clothes. At some point they stop caressing and separately take their clothes off. They lie down again and carry on kissing and caressing. You see his hand disappear between her legs and guess from the regular movements that he is rhythmically stroking her clitoris. She stretches and purrs in approval then settles to become almost motionless as she concentrates on the sensation that is building inside her. 'Stop,' she says, 'come inside me,' and she urges him to climb over her and insert his penis into her vagina. She pushes her pelvis up towards him and you can see the in/out of his thrusting. If you look at her face you realise that she has gone into a world of the interior, her eyes are glazed, her attention far away, where only sexual feelings matter. 'Help me a little,' she asks. He accordingly shifts one thigh and inserts his hand between their bodies. As he continues to thrust, his arm drums to the rhythm he is whipping up

on her clitoris. Suddenly she starts to come, with her body shuddering and her head thrown back, breathing rapididly. When she hits the high point of coming, she screams. And as long as she goes on screaming her young lover does not let up. He thrusts and fingers with great energy. He drives on and forward, on and forward. It is only when he is quite clear her climax is over that he withdraws his hand, closes his eyes and focuses on his own thrusting. When he climaxes, he does so in a quick series of spurts and hard gasps. 'Oh,' he cries, short and sharp, then collapses on her in a happy heap. She folds her arms around him and gathers his limp body in to hers.

Does this scene disturb you? Does it feel wrong to read it? Forbidden? Upsetting? If you are not sure of your emotion, read the description again.

Male masturbation

Let your imagination take you to the far side of a bedroom. You are hidden but you can see, from your hiding place, a man lying on the bed. You know that this is for real, this is not an actor from a porn movie in spite of his being young and handsome. He is moving about a lot. In fact, from your distance, it looks as if he is feeling uncomfortable. You zoom in closer and see that the reason he is moving is because he is masturbating. But this is not some still and passive jerk-off. This young male is moving his entire body as he moves his cock. He kneels up to manipulate his penis, one hand doing the task while the other roams all over his body, stroking, pushing, kneading. He bends over and continues to pull on his penis as he leans on all fours. As he speeds up the rhythm of his cock he starts to move his entire body, backwards and forwards, into his hand. Now he gets up off the bed and leans against it, juts his cock hard out into the room as he pounds away, his hips jerking his penis into and out of the cylinder of his hand. He dances across the room moving that penis in and out of his grasp until with a great explosion he comes while he is arched up on one foot in a kind of arabesque.

You may think this sounds an unlikely visualisation of male masturbation but it is based on one of the Glide Foundation films and it is real. The young man filmed was a ballet dancer and put his entire body into self-satisfaction. How did you feel about it? Is there another way in which you would prefer to see a male masturbating? One that feels more realistic to you?

Alternative male masturbation

A man is washing himself in the bath. After he has efficiently soaped his body he leans back to rest a bit in the suds. And relax. Slowly, his hands creep down to his genitals. While one hand holds his penis at the base the other lazily pulls on the penis several times until it stands by

itself. Still holding it at the base he uses the other hand, palm down, to rub around and over the head of the penis, lemon-squeezer style. He's in no particular hurry. And he is very deliberate. Next he pulls up with the underneath hand while continuing to rub and circle on the head, then pushes down again with the lower hand. He's got two very precise actions going simultaneously with his busy hands. The rest of his body is still and quite soon straining forwards. Now he's not so slow. He is much more excited and his two hands get rough. He's gripping his cock and moving hard and fast, very fast. Surely that must hurt, you think, as you see him pumping in a blur of speed. Now his body is keeping time with the action, chucking a little bathwater over the side. It's so fast you know he's out of control. It would be hard to stop now. Suddenly and quickly his penis erupts into an arc of pure fluid jetting towards the end of the tub. As it does so he subsides, groaning into the by-now tepid water.

Does this description feel more realistic? More like what you might expect? And what did you feel? Shock? Disgust? Pleasure? Or acceptance? Don't get side-tracked into thinking this is the right way to masturbate. Any way is the right way. There is no one typical way.

Female masturbation

She is 30-something and plump. She steps into the shower

and soaps herself luxuriously, creating a lot of foam which she rinses off while tracking the pinpoints of water from the shower head across her skin for a long while. As she steps out of the shower cubicle she helps herself to a warm towel from the towel rail and wanders into the bedroom, comfortably drying herself. She strips the top sheet from the bed and places a dry towel over the bottom sheet. She gathers up a box of tissues and some massage oil, which she places on the bedside table. Now she makes herself comfortable, leaning back on to a circle of cushions. Using some of the oil she rubs it all over her body and especially around her breasts. She squeezes and kneads her breasts and evidently gets a lot of pleasure from doing this because you can see her relax and sink back. In fact she so enjoys this that it takes a while before she moves her hands down to her genitals. When she does so she holds her labia open with her left hand so that the pink interior is exposed. Then with one finger of the right hand she gently, oh so gently, starts to rub on her clitoris. As she gets more excited she pulls her labia up hard and arches her back a little. Dissatisfied with this, she shifts her left hand underneath her left thigh and reaching up with it from underneath, puts a finger into her vagina and pulls downwards. She gasps almost immediately, such is the easy turn-on this gives her, and accelerates her twirling and rubbing of the clitoris with the right hand. Now she jerks her pelvis towards that thrusting top finger, and each time she does

← shower

so gasps as she pulls against that constraining bottom finger. Her head falls backwards, her mouth opens a little and her hips jerk convulsively as she comes again and again. She doesn't stop the stimulation though – she goes right on rubbing and climaxing many times until finally the climaxes die away. Awkwardly, she removes the arm that has become trapped underneath her satisfied pelvis, with an effort heaves her legs together and lies panting as if getting her breath back.

This is the real masturbation pattern of a real woman. Did it hold any surprises for you? Did you feel embarrassed by viewing it? Was it like anything you have seen or experienced? Try rerunning it to check out your reactions. Now try this alternative.

Visualise the same woman, stepping into the same shower. She goes through the same bathing routine, rubbing herself with foaming soap and luxuriously showering it off with the carefully directed shower head. Only this time she doesn't get out of the shower because she's become far too interested in the tiny pin prick of sensuality on her genitals from the shower water. She holds the shower head at crotch position and squats slightly so that her legs are as wide as they can be without letting her fall over. The shower plays upon her labia, the outer end of her vagina and her clitoris. But presumably the sensation isn't strong enough for she does two things. The first is she adjusts the flow of water so that it spurts out much harder and the second is that she holds her labia open with two fingers so that the water cannot miss her clitoris. After a while she stands very still and shuts her eyes. You sense that the drumming of the tiny water jets is stirring up an acute sensation. Suddenly she staggers and puts out a hand to avoid slipping. But she carries on drumming the jets at her clitoris. Almost immediately she starts jerking her pelvis forward into the spray. 'Oh,' she says softly, 'oh.' It doesn't last for long but it was there. Now she feels so overcome that she turns the shower off, sits on the shower tray and clasps and presses her hands between her legs. 'Wow,' she says, 'wow.'

You have visualised a completely different masturbation pattern to the one described before and yet it has been experienced by the same woman. There are many different ways of climaxing – not only for different people but many of them for the same person. Human beings are creative.

If you have masturbated, how many different ways have you ever done it? If you haven't experimented, perhaps, after this, you might like to try.

Rough sex
A couple in their mid-30s settle down on a mattress in the

living room. The mattress is covered with a sheepskin rug, there are plants dotted about the room and you can tell it's afternoon from the angle of the sun shining through the curtain-free windows. You take a quick peer through the window and discover, with relief, that it is on the second storey and not overlooked. 'I'm giving you a treat today,' says the woman and produces a bottle of massage oil. She oils and greases his body and works on it for a good 10 minutes, firmly pushing and gliding her hands over and around his back. When she turns him over to cover his front you see that he has an erection. She laughs and massages his front, eventually including the erection in the massage. When you take a closer look at the man's face you see his eyes are open and glazed with pleasure. You also see that his expression is changing; he is deciding to change the action. 'Come here,' he says and pulls his woman's naked body on to his. She slides and swims across the oil slick that soon coats them both. His erection is standing up harder than ever. Next he starts to press her down towards that erection so that it catches between her legs and then comes free again as he slides her up towards his chest. Up and down they slide until both are panting and flushed. 'It's so hot in here,' she gasps, raising a hand to wipe the perspiration from her face. 'That's how I like it,' he says abruptly, and catching her arms turns her sideways on to the mattress. Without waiting for her reaction he puts his large hand between her legs and begins to rub his entire fist up and down. And his movements are hard. At one stage he stops, spits on to his hand and rubs the spit into her genitals. She is gasping with sharp intakes of breath now as he shoves that hand backwards and forwards, scraping across her labia and grinding across her clitoris, backwards and forwards. He heaves her up on to all fours, moves behind and penetrates her vagina from the rear. His fist continues to batter her genitals from the front and he crashes into her from behind as if he is a battering ram. Her neck is arching upwards, her mouth opening and suddenly she screams piercingly, over and over again. She shrieks and howls, she is so loud she is disturbing. Her body actually shakes and ricochets with the force of her climax, each contraction shooting her body forward and then back again. And she doesn't stop, she continues jerking abruptly forwards until her screaming sounds quite worn out and she can hardly move. Her partner, who has been thrusting so hard that she has moved halfway across the mattress, judders his way to a climax, shouting 'Oh,' at the top of his voice with every involuntary contraction of his ejaculation. A short while after they have collapsed in a heap, she crawls into his sheltering arm and looks up at him with enormous satisfaction. 'Mm,' she says, licking her lips. 'Mm.' He grins and closes his eyes.

Is this how you have sex? Can you let go like this couple? Or is your pattern quieter and softer? What do you think such rough sex might feel like? Could it be an option for you? If the answer is no, think about why not. Would you fear it? Would it turn you on at all? Or is the following visualisation more recognisable?

The fairy fuck

A hotel room – the door opens and a petite dark-haired woman walks in, followed by a large older man. In close-up, you realise she is Japanese. The couple put down their suitcases and she experimentally sits on the bed. 'It's good,' she says, bouncing experimentally. 'Nice and soft.' 'Good,' he comments, 'I'll be able to sleep.' The couple unpacks. She puts on her white nightdress, he his pyjama bottoms. They climb into bed and as he is about to put out the light, she stops him. 'Not yet darling.' He looks grumpy but acquiesces. She leans over him and kisses him. He responds a little reluctantly. You can practically see him glancing at his watch. But he kisses back. Emboldened she kisses again and this time he embraces her more deeply. He kisses her long and passionately, so passionately that her little body, inside its white cotton, begins to squirm. 'Take this off,' he urges and, seizing the garment, drags it over her head. Without it you realise what a perfect body this young woman has – but in miniature. Placed against the man's larger frame she looks like a little fairy. He carries on kissing her and while doing so hauls her little body up on top of his. He pushes her hand towards his pyjama bottoms. She fumbles for the cord, undoes it and then slides down his body to pull off the cotton trousers. His erection is standing up – he is very broad with a wide head to his penis. 'Come on darling,' he fumbles impatiently between her legs, rubs her briefly with his forefinger, withdraws the forefinger and looks at it. It is glistening with moisture. 'Ummm,' he says, and puts the finger his mouth. 'Ummm.' He flirts with her and she is shy, but pleased. She shows her arousal by squirming her rear even harder until he seizes her tiny bottom, covering the buttocks with his big hands and quite gently steers her down, on to his large cock. Each gasps as the tiny cunt encloses the big erection. She sits astride him for a while, moving energetically up and down. You catch glimpses of this large penis poking up her as she waves her buttocks energetically in a kind of frenzied massage. 'Lie down on me darling,' grunts the man. 'Give me a kiss.' She stretches over him and he kisses her passionately, then pushes her with his hands upwards and downwards so that she is rubbing full frontal across him. 'Don't stop,' she gasps. Her tiny frame suddenly stops, freezes then quite slowly jerks – one, two, three. She says not a word, but her mouth is wide open in a wordless cry. He is watching this with love. And when she is finished, he pulls her up, off his penis and kisses her with affection. 'Better now darling?' he asks jokingly and she smiles slowly and affectionately too. 'Don't you want to come?'

she asks. 'No, I don't think I do,' he replies. 'I'll save it for another occasion.'

> *What were you expecting to happen with this couple? Did you think that the older man might be going to take some kind of advantage of her? Who would you see as the protagonist here? And how did this sexual pattern feel to you? Was it different? Or was it familiar? Is this the kind of sex you enjoy? Or would you like to enjoy it? Was it easier to relate to than the previous scene?*

Cunnilingus

We see a tall thin young man with lanky long hair and a drooping moustache walk hand in hand with his long-haired girlfriend into their bedroom. Outside the door we pause for a minute and listen in. He is coaxing her to take her clothes off. She says she doesn't want to, she's busy. 'Oh come on honey,' he pleads. 'Let's cuddle.' After a bit more grumbling, she reluctantly agrees. We go through the door as they lie down together. They kiss and cuddle but she's still not terribly interested. The young man looks at her knowingly and says, 'I know what you want.' Without saying anything more he slides down her body and parts her legs. We look at her genitals, nestling in a halo of luxuriant dark curls. He raises his left arm so that his hand curves above her clitoris and, with thumb and fore-finger, draws back the top of her pubic mound, exposing

the tiny glistening button that is her clitoris. She puts her hands on his head and her fingers wrap themselves in his hair. He lowers his head to her crotch and pointing his tongue, pushes upward with it against her clitoris. 'Oh yes,' she says. Now she is interested. His head with his tongue projecting forward moves up and down, up and down, always running up and along the underside of her tiny clitoris. Which is not now so tiny. You can actually see it swell to twice the size. Now he pushes his tongue up first one side of the clitoris, then the other side. Then he twirls his tongue in tiny circles on the top of the clitoral head. She is breathing hard now, her left hand repeatedly rubbing around and around her left breast. He glances up and sees that her eyes are closed and that she is far off, away in her head. He goes back to the original licking up underneath the clitoris and over the head before retreating downwards again. She loves this and curls her legs around his head, almost throttling him. He manfully keeps going as she begins to jerk her hips. 'More, please,' she gasps. 'More.' He obliges by ramming his head and tongue up and down even faster. If there were sexual stamina records this guy would be breaking them. Finally she gasps, 'I'm coming, I'm coming,' and then moans 'oh,' 'oh,' 'oh,' in time to tiny jerks of her buttocks and hips. He gives signs he is about to stop. 'No,' she shrieks and pushes his head down, 'keep going.' He laboriously carries on and she rewards him by quietly experiencing several more neat jerks of the buttocks. Finally he is allowed to halt and she draws him up so that his head is next to hers. You see that his face is hot and sweaty and that his mouth and lower part of his face covered with her juices. 'You're gorgeous, Roy,' she says, and taking his head between her hands kisses him square on her own love lubes. Roy is almost too tired to notice though we are told that he does go on to have missionary-position sex with her for his own orgasm at the end of this scene.

Is this how oral sex goes for you? Would you use other techniques that Roy omitted? How do you feel about the mess, the lubrication, the juxtaposition of genitals and lips? The idea of tasting the other person's interior juices? Have you ever tasted your own? If not, have a think about why not. Give it a go.

Fellatio

We zoom in on an older woman and a younger man. He is a lot younger, possibly 20 years younger. She is youthful-looking but middle-aged. They are walking naked into a living room. They are laughing, carrying glasses of wine and touching affectionately as they walk towards the sofa. She gestures towards it and laughingly pushes him to sit down. He knocks back a long draught of wine then puts the glass down by the side of his seat. He's smiling wide and looking amused and appreciative of what is to come.

He pats the side of the sofa inviting her next to him but she declines and sinks to her knees in front of him. Putting a hand on his thigh she urges him to shuffle forward on his bottom so that his pelvis is half off the edge of the sofa with his genitals protruding towards her. Neither appear remotely embarrassed but look instead as if they anticipate a really fun time. Pushing open his legs so that they are wide, she lowers her mouth on to his flaccid penis. It is quite small at present and appears to fit rather well. She smiles with her mouth full and holding the base with one hand, draws her mouth back from it. She also slides her other hand in underneath his testicles and on each up movement of her head, moves the hand up and away underneath the testicles. He reacts almost immediately to her skill and his penis telescopes before our eyes. A little more sucking and rubbing and his erection is so erect it already looks at bursting point. It has gone a deep purple and is straining. At one point she stops, takes her mouth away and looks at the tip. The entrance to the penis is gleaming and lubricated. She squeezes him slightly and beads of fluid appear in the tiny hole. 'Don't stop,' he groans and tries to move her head back down. Now she is sliding her head up and down to meet the hand gripping the base of the penis. She is pumping hard on him and sucking like a vacuum cleaner. Her hand slides up to meet her head coming down and the combined sucking, rubbing and swirling of opposite movements vacuums him completely out of his mind so that he erupts into her mouth. As he ejaculates, she keeps still and concentrates on holding his cum in her mouth. When his penis slowly deflates, she helps him out and then spits his cum neatly on to a Kleenex. He is slumped against the back of the sofa, his head back, breathing hard but slowing down. She rests her head, tired from hard movement, against his naked thigh. His limp cock has fallen behind her and gleams with saliva and cum. His hand raises slowly and pats her quietly on the shoulder. She nods her head silently. They don't need to talk. They are comfortable.

> *What are your thoughts here? Is this a usual picture of oral sex? How did you feel about the relationship between an older woman and a younger man? What thoughts/emotions went through your head? Was there anything that felt wrong about what you saw? Could you deal with giving or receiving fellatio?*

Homosexuality

Two gay men are sprawled across a king-size bed looking at a magazine. They are in their 30s, sturdily built and one is a little taller than the other. The bigger guy has a shaven head while the other shows off a college-boy hairstyle. They are naked and their buttocks gleam intensely white in contrast to the tan on the rest of their body. As your gaze travels along their backsides, your eyes move from those

pert white buttocks to take a look at their reading matter. They are looking at a gay magazine and in particular at the centrefold. Pictured on it is a young, handsome, well-groomed and exceedingly well-hung porno-movie star. The guys are chuckling as they show the centrefold off to each other. They soon grow bored and move on to other spreads; one catches their attention and they stop flicking through the book. You sense that each is getting turned on by the picture, since their bodies go very still. The smaller man grins then rubs the other guy's hand over his now enlarging cock. What is it that is such a turn-on? Peering over their shoulders you see a spread of photos, depicting a well-built black man sliding his muscular penis in between the buttocks of a smaller white man. The pictures portray the in and out of penile thrusting and the last of the series shows the black man head back, gripping the white guy around the waist and straining him against his body as he evidently comes.

'I like that,' says our big guy. 'Yeah,' agrees the younger guy and turning towards his friend kisses him passionately, long and full on the lips. 'It's a good one.' The couple kiss a great deal, on the mouth, on the neck and on the chest. As they do so they rub and pull at each other's nipples until these stand up with small erections of their own. The big guy puts his head down and sucks on his friend's breast, until his friend is gasping and squirming with sensation. The big guy has lost his erection though while his friend's looks swollen enough for two. The friend, on seeing this, drops to his knees and swiftly sucks and manipulates his mate's cock. The erection returns, unfolding like an inflatable. Now the big guy spits on his hand, rubs that hand across his friend's rear, and then, having sucked on his forefinger first, puts this finger, dropping spittle, into his friend's back passage. He slips and twists and winds his way, inch by inch, into the depths of his friend's resistant arse. 'Stop, wait,' are the gasped commands when the pressing finger gets too much. But it doesn't wait long to go on, and soon that probing digit is stretching and widening his friend's rosebud rear. He is moving his finger round and round the immediate inside of the anus, conjuring up every shred of sensual feeling from this highly sensuous region. 'Oh my god,' his friend is gasping, 'oh my god.' When he hears this, Big guy reckons his friend is ready to receive him, and buttering up his cock with gobs of saliva he carefully pushes his penis into his mate's now helpless backside. His mate is still lying on his back and raises his legs high while the big guy pushes in as if he were having hetero intercourse. As he presses deeper, his friend's eyes almost roll back in their sockets thanks to the deep sensation that is sending him nearly out of his skull. Big guy's first withdrawal and then second thrust is tentative. Small guy has to get used to him. But his arse eases up and soon Big guy is thrusting, with Small guy's legs wrapped like snakes around his broad shoulders. It only takes about four deep thrusts for Small guy to go wild with his climax. He wedges his hands somewhere in between the two of them and attempts to catch the ejaculate that is swamping his torso. Big guy looks down and likes what he sees and shoving his head back gives a last almighty heave and roars, bucking and jerking as he does so. After the sex has finished the two guys lie together for a while. Big guy turns to his friend, gives him a peck on the cheek and says, 'That was great honey,' and you can tell that he means it.

Does this feel like porn when you read it? Or not? Is the experience utterly alien? Or do you own up to feelings of fascination? In case you doubt that men can have sex like this, don't. They can and do. Could you ever imagine yourself doing this?

Please don't be afraid of owning the truth to yourself. Imagining it does not mean you will ever do it. Many of us are actually bisexual yet so well conditioned by the society we've grown up in that those other sexual feelings never get permission to come on out. Or is it the last kind of sex you have ever wanted to know about? Look hard at all your feelings. Where are you on the Kinsey scale of gender inclination? Gay, bisexual or straight?

Lesbianism

The first thing you hear are screams of laughter and the drumming of feet. Then more screams and giggles and 'got you.' The sound of pouncing and tickling and someone screaming hysterically at the top of their voice. When you look round the door two women in their late 20s, one of average build, the other very skinny, are chasing each other round the room. They are fully clothed in tight cotton tops and loose-fitting trousers. The skinny woman with a mop of short curly hair stumbles on to the sofa, where she is mercilessly tickled by her friend. She is so helpless with laughter that soon she begs her friend to stop. 'If you don't stop,' she says, 'I'll wet myself. I can hardly control myself.' 'Please, please,' she begs. 'Oh, I can see a little bit of wet,' her friend teases, pretending to look hard at Skinny's crotch. 'You can't, can you?' her helpless partner asks, both frightened and unbelieving and still giggling weakly. 'Not really,' says her mate and takes pity by stopping her manic finger action. 'Oh, thank god,' Skinny sighs with relief. It's an effort to haul herself upright. She leans exhausted on her friend's shoulder for a couple of minutes and then nudges her mouth on to her friend's neck. She nuzzles into it, absent-mindedly kissing and softly biting it. Her tickling partner doesn't take a lot of notice to begin with but relaxes into the sensation. Then she turns her head swiftly sideways, puts a hand under her friend's chin and draws Skinny into a huge kiss.

doesn't
want
to
be known

Skinny melts like a jelly on a hot day until she flops right down into her friend's body. Her friend stops and appraises her. And smiles. It's the sort of smile that shows she is feeling very powerful with this friend whom she can reduce to a heap. Slowly and deliberately she leans forward and kisses Skinny hard and square on the lips. Then she bites, hard enough to make Skinny scream and leap back. 'Why did you do that?' 'Because you're good enough to eat,' says her friend. 'So I'm going to do just that.' And is back to chasing a hysterical Skinny halfway across the room. This time when she gets her friend in an arm lock in a corner Skinny kisses and then bites right back. 'Bitch,' screams her friend but she's smiling. Holding Skinny's arms behind her back, she unties the drawstring on Skinny's loose-fitting cotton trousers and gets her friend to step out of them. Since Skinny is not wearing panties you can see that on her almost skeletal pelvis there is a great bush of brilliant red pubic hair. Her friend looks at this admiringly. Meanwhile the owner of the red pubes has fallen silent. 'You are gorgeous, you know,' says her lover and proceeds to take off her own cotton trousers. Leading her mate back to the sofa she sits her down then sits next to her. With one arm around her shoulders, she kisses Skinny a lot more until Skinny is squirming. 'Rub me, Matty,' pleads Skinny. Matty obliges. She puts her fingers into Skinny's flaming pubes and rubs backwards and forwards but very, very lightly as if she is skimming the tip of her finger over the surface of Skinny's genitals. Skinny looks intent. Matty changes the up and down movement of her finger to circling with a barely-there lightness on the tip of Skinny's clitoris and Skinny almost passes out with sensuality. She lies absolutely still, so still that you wonder if she has fainted, but as Matty continues with the delicate finger work Skinny spreads her arms and legs out wide, and climaxes from the very heart of her body. You can see her contract in ripples that flood across her abdomen and out through her arms. And her cries are wrenched from the back of her throat: wordless, meaningless sounds that pierce the air exactly as the climax appears to be piercing her body. Then very, very lightly she subsides and is quite silent. Her friend settles calmly down beside her. Within a minute Skinny turns to Matty and puts both arms around her. 'I love you Matty,' she says. 'I love you.'

> *Did this feel more or less shocking than the two guys having sex? Was there anything unexpected in this scene? Did anything feel wrong about this love-making between two women? Or did it feel entirely natural to you? Did it turn you off, turn you on, or leave you indifferent? How do you feel now? What do you think about the fact that one of the women has not climaxed?*

A threesome

There's a party. People are singing, dancing, drinking, smoking and talking intently, trying to make themselves heard above the hubbub. We close in on one particular small group, seated on a huge sofa at the back of the room where they are half hidden by the sheer numbers packing the room. They aren't saying much these three, just smiling softly, drinking wine and watching the others. There are two good-looking dark-haired men in their late 30s, dressed in soft black tee-shirts and black slacks. And a woman, aged around 40, wearing a halter-top that leaves her back bare and a skirt down to the ground. When your eyes get used to the cigarette smoke you notice that one of the men is caressing the woman's hand while the other is softly stroking her thigh underneath the folds of the material. What's more, the two guys are caressing each other's hands lying along the top of the sofa. No one is in a hurry. The woman puts down her wine glass and lies back. They stroke some more. She closes her eyes and basks in their touch. She virtually purrs. One man leans his head forward and kisses her on the mouth. She responds with surprising strength considering the lack of any other move of her own. Across her head the two guys' eyes meet. One of them gestures and points upwards. 'Upstairs,' he suggests. The other nods faintly, and with his arms firmly around the woman says, 'Let's go, Hilde.' She smiles faintly, nods and gathers up her bag. The three cross the crowded room, smile at acquaintances and walk upstairs to the comparative peace and quiet of low lighting and empty rooms. In the big dark bedroom the door is locked and the three move towards the bed. One man clasps Hilde from behind and she lies back in his protective arms. The other stands in front of her and clasps both the woman and the man in his embrace. He stands front on to her, but his arms caress his male friend. She puts her arms around his neck and kisses him. Long kisses later the two men take off their trousers. But when she attempts to disrobe from her evening skirt, one of them stops her. 'No, he says, leave it on.' But he does help her step out of her panties. While one man continues to kiss her and fondle her through her clothes, the other lifts up her skirt and caresses her buttocks. Leaning forward he curves his arm around underneath the skirt and you can tell from the movement in the material that he is slowly stroking her vagina in long relaxed strokes. Occasionally you get glimpses of her long legs as the skirt rises and falls. She is finding it harder and harder to remain standing upright. She staggers a little and the man kissing now holds her steady. She is moaning and softly sighing, and getting more turned on by the minute. Her moans turn to distinct cries and the cries get more and more urgent, rapid and loud. The men are telling her how attractive she is and the more they talk about how much they desire her, the more carried away she becomes. She really can hardly stand now so the front man sits on the floor and helps her down with him. He slips off his boxers and, lying flat, gently pulls her on top of him. With a billowing of her evening skirt over his abdomen she settles down slowly, her cunt closing down on his penis. The man at the back of her is helping her get into place. He is holding her hips and as he does so looks at the other male who smiles lazily, but with pure lust, back. Now the man at the rear lifts up that evening skirt and slowly drives his penis into her rear. He manages this without any great difficulty. You get the sense that she has done this many times before. But no matter how many times, the sensation of being so filled, in both front and back passages really does it for this woman. She stays quite still while the rear guy drives into her and comes quickly to his orgasm. As he shouts his climax the other guy who has been watching is visibly moved. As soon as the rear guy has withdrawn he encourages her to move rapidly on top of him so that she can whip him into his own climax. She does this while now fingering herself so that she can get an orgasm of her own. She comes very quickly indeed and the man underneath, seeing her climax, seizes her by the hips and ejaculates deep into her. Both are crying out as they come. When it's over, the rear guy helps her wipe herself down with a tissue and then helps his male friend. For a short time the three lie relaxed together on the floor. Until one of them says, 'We should get back to the party.'

Is this how you imagined a threesome? If it's not, how does your version differ? Is this something you would like to experience? Or are you happy to leave it to others? Is there anything about this scene you are uncomfortable with? What role do you think the woman is playing? What do you think she means to the two men? And what does she get out of this?

Sex in old age

A much older couple are drinking tea and smoking a cigarette. They are naked. You would guess that she is around 60 and he is probably 70. Their bodies, those of older people, are wrinkled but tanned. Their faces light up when they smile, making both look very attractive. They also look very affectionately towards each other. They pat each other's hands often, kiss, cuddle and joke together. Ultimately she gets up and pulls him after her.

They are both grinning as they walk into the bedroom. This older couple spends a good half hour caressing and giving each other a lot of hand manipulation; she gives him a lot of oral sex before his erection gets really hard. And when he comes before she does, he continues afterwards to bring her to orgasm with his hand. They seem open and natural and comfortable with their bodies. They clearly have a great time together and enjoy each other a lot. You go away after they finish thinking what a great marriage this couple have. You can almost feel the tangible affection

that they express towards each other through their sex. So it comes as quite a surprise when you hear that they are not married, they are very good old friends who have got together with the sole purpose of having sex for one of the institute's films.

> *Does it shock you that a much older man and woman could have such enjoyable sex without being in a committed relationship? How do you think that they coped with not having perfect bodies? It's one thing for a long-term partner to be used to the shape of your body – you get to feel comfortable with him/her. But a new partner? What will they think about our lumps and bumps? And yet this couple seemed absolutely fine together. What does it take to behave in this way?*

You have now read through a short collection of visualisations. Ideally there should be many more, in fact an entire volume full. Here, alas, we don't have the space. But I hope you begin to get an idea of what I'm aiming at. You have probably read the visualisations to yourself, in private. Do you notice any difference in the way you were feeling about the sexual activities described at the end of the series compared to the feelings you experienced at the beginning? Were you feeling less turned on as you continued with your reading? And more able to look at what was going on dispassionately?

If you don't notice much change in your reactions, this may be because I can only present a short selection here and I would suggest you go back to the beginning and read through again. After this I would suggest that if you haven't already done so you read through the visualisations once more only this time with other people – that you all read and then discuss them as a group. In between each subject, stop and talk about what you've just imagined and voice your feelings – the thoughts, fears, hopes that the descriptions evoke.

Shameless

It is when you can talk about these very taboo subjects absolutely openly with no sense of embarrassment or shame, no sense that you need to excuse yourself, that you know your attitudes to sex are changing. You do need to temper your discussion to what other people may be able to accept. But my own experience is that it is quite possible to talk explicitly about sex, without using crude words or expressions, in a way that can be acceptable. I certainly know that when *you* feel comfortable with sex, other people settle down and start to feel comfortable too.

JOIN THE GROWN-UPS

And it is this less judgemental attitude towards sex that allows you to look at sexual situations and sexual problems with greater ease than you have managed before. One of the ultimate tests is when you can manage to talk to your parents about sex. I am not suggesting you go into explicit details you know will shock and offend them. *They* haven't read the visualisation programme. But you are all grown-ups now. You should be able to feel comfortable enough to hold some conversation about sex.

And in case you think I've included the visualisations as unadulterated porn, here is the theory behind them. It is only by becoming familiar with sexual behaviours that you can get used to them. And it is only by getting used to these that the heat, the sting, goes out of such activities. Instead of seeing them as shameful, they become simply instances of sexual behaviour. The guilt-laden judgements that you may have unconsciously brought to them ease away. So my reason for writing the visualisations is to give you an inkling in these pages of what the SAR programme does with much greater efficiency and immediacy through film.

When sex goes wrong

Who is in control of your body?
Have you ever dreamed of dressing up your partner in a black mask, fixing straps between their buttocks and tying them to the bedpost before fucking the life out of them? Come on – admit it. You can do so here because no one will ever know. But even if you don't admit it, I wouldn't mind betting the reality is that you have never dared to actually do this. Thinking is one thing – doing quite another. So what do you suppose is stopping you?

The answer might be, common sense. You know absolutely for certain that your partner would run a mile the minute you whipped the cat o' nine tails out. And it's a good answer. But suppose you don't know this, suppose you only think this because you believe that only abnormal people would do such outrageous things and you would rather die than have anyone think you were so outrageous. Who or what exactly is preventing you now?

Let's go further. Let's suppose your partner secretly felt the same and was only waiting for you to make the suggestion. There you are, two people who might be enjoy-

ing an exceptional sexual intimacy and yet you are completely blocked. You would hurt no third party if you followed your real desire but something inside is stopping
you. That something is the force of what you believe to be
public opinion.

Constrained, controlled and prescribed sex
Public opinion may turn out to be a powerful meme. It can
certainly dictate any number of opposite beliefs depending
on what part of the world you live in. If you believed that
everyone in your country went to an s & m club every Saturday night, then the odds are you'd be right along with
them. Or look at it another way. You have no trouble with
doing sex in the missionary position – everyone knows that
this is *the* prescribed Western method of having sex. So
imagine visiting a society where everyone found the missionary position entirely shocking and you were the only
one to use it. Wouldn't the censure of everyone around
seem ridiculous? But as you thought about it a little more,
might you not feel yourself being sucked into the idea that
missionary sex could be depraved and wrong, in certain
circumstances? We belong to a species that so much wants
to feel itself in line that we sometimes go along with ideas
we know in our gut to be nonsense.

Now I want to complicate the issue. So far I've been
arguing about the dramatic decisions we may wrestle with
in our sex lives. But suppose our predilections are the

opposite. Suppose, in fact, sex isn't all that interesting to us. Have there never been times when you really wished you didn't have to perform that night? Aren't there occasionally, if you're truthful, times when you'd prefer to curl up with a good book and a box of chocolates?

Some people don't feel sex is their priority. They are perfectly comfortable with a life that includes little of it. Yet other people find it hard to let them be. These more laid-back, less sexually driven individuals either get pressured into finding a sex partner or made to feel they are seriously lacking if they don't. Men foolish enough to reveal they have a short penis or a low sex drive become the butt of jokes, the subject of innuendo. Colleagues make fun of them behind their back. Women who rarely experience orgasm are not infrequently made to feel as if something is seriously wrong with them. And these criticisms are often made when the women themselves are not terribly bothered about their quieter sex lives. They are actually penalised for being well-adjusted.

Somewhere along the line the idea has seeped through that those men and women who are not overly sexual are inadequate. But the truth is that these are normal people. They are at one end of the human spectrum of sexuality. This doesn't stop others dictating what choices should be made for them. And the minute anyone starts feeling s/he *ought* to be performing better it is because s/he is being subjected to equally as powerful a controlling constraint as those men and women who don't dare to snap on the handcuffs.

Sexual spectrums

Every jot of research into the patterns of human sexuality shows that men and women experience extraordinarily diverse patterns of sexuality. Alfred Kinsey, who did major research in the late 1940s and early 1950s, deduced, after taking thousands of case histories, that there is a spectrum of human sexuality as there is of colour or health or intelligence. It is as human to want to play extreme sex games as it is to want sex only twice a year. Yet I bet that many of you will almost immediately reject the thought as nonsense. That is how deeply our beliefs are entrenched.

> ### KINSEY'S SEXUAL ORIENTATION SPECTRUM
> Another of Kinsey's spectrums measured sexual orientation. He saw normal human sexuality running from heterosexuality on one side of the spectrum through bisexuality in the middle, right across to homosexuality on the opposite side.

Other surveys have shown that as far as acts of sex are concerned, frequency ranged between none per year right through to five acts per day, every day. These latter were not all acts of intercourse but included masturbation and related to a younger rather than an older age range, with a few notable exceptions. It might be true to say that no act of sex at all, ever, is abnormal, except those that harm someone else. Since we are a race that must perpetuate itself through sex, the only real perversity might be never to have sex at all.

SIZE MATTERS

There are other spectrums of sexuality too. Penis size ranges from the microphallus to the 12-inch/30-cm ruler. Different races are found to have different shapes and lengths of penis. Clitoral size ranges too – the average clitoris is one and a half inches long – and labia also vary greatly in size and shape. As long as they are all in working order who is to say that anything is wrong with any of them?

When problems arise

If you have a lower sex drive and your partner also has a lower sex drive then there is no problem. You match each other perfectly. The real difficulties arise when you:

- get together with a partner whose sex drive does not perfectly match yours;
- find a partner who is too inhibited to say what is really on his/her mind;
- feel so pressurised that your sexual performance wilts.

Looked at from the starting point of ideas – all of the individuals experiencing these various situations are being affected by notions or beliefs. It is the ideas they possess about sexuality that trouble them – and not the actual sexual performance.

CASE HISTORY

A couple was referred for sex therapy because he complained she didn't ever want sex and she complained their sex life didn't work for her. On questioning it turned out that the couple regularly had intercourse and she regularly enjoyed orgasm. Their sex life did work. What therefore was wrong? The husband explained that his wife never made the moves in bed, never initiated sex. He explained this several times. She, on the other hand, revealed that although she could be physically aroused she didn't feel really emotionally turned on by this man. He continued to moan and whine about what a bad wife she was because she didn't want sex all the time, and he did. He sounded like a demanding little boy. You began to get an idea about why he wasn't an instant turn-on.

When we analysed their complaints, the problem boiled down to his ideas about the kind of sexual service a good wife gives her man. As a favoured younger child he had been spoon-fed; his mother had done everything for him. Now he expected his wife to do the same.

The meme – he believed a good wife derived her pleasure from her man's pleasure – literally, that if he felt erotic so too did she. And if he needed a lot of reassurance in the shape of sexuality, well then, naturally she would want to give it, all the time, wouldn't she?

(This couple learned to build on the areas that functioned well. He worked on not asking for sex so often and also became better at giving her climaxes. She in turn accepted that this was an anxious man who needed a lot of reassurance. She made a point of giving him more reassurance in general so that eventually he didn't need so much sexual reassurance because he finally felt she cared about him.)

If we want to examine what is going wrong in our sex lives we need to begin with the entire concept of a sexual belief system. If you can identify your own or your partner's sexual beliefs you get an inkling of the memes that are driving them – and, at second-hand, the memes that are therefore also driving you, whether or not you approve of them.

COMMON SEX MYTHS

Here are a few of the memes that I have come across during 20 years of sex counselling.

If I do anything s/he wants in bed s/he will stay faithful.

If I refuse to do something s/he wants in bed, then s/he definitely will leave me.

If I cannot rise to the occasion every time I am not a real man.

If I cannot climax at the same time as my partner I am not doing sex properly.

If I ejaculate before 20 minutes of thrusting, I am a poor lover.

If I cannot swallow semen during oral sex, my man will think me a poor lover.

I can prove I am independent by having a succession of one-night stands.

If I don't constantly introduce novelty to the sex act, I will lose my partner's interest.

If I constantly initiate new sexual ideas my partner will believe me a slut.

If I don't constantly initiate new sexual ideas my partner will believe me unmanly.

How do we avoid falling into these traps? Is it even possible to do so? The realistic answer is that we all grow up in specific families and specific cultures. We can't help absorbing ideas from that culture. We do so from the very start of life as tiny children. So the first step is to realise that in order to make adult life work sometimes we need to

change our ideas and move on. We can only do that provided we know in the first place what those ideas consist of. A little self-analysis is called for. Take a look at my sexual memes test in chapter 2 and when you have identified some of the sexual ideas that have influenced you during your upbringing, move on to the section below.

Know your own sexual beliefs

Read through the lists of options that follow and mark out those that apply to your background and upbringing. Please note, there is no one right answer to these choices. You may want to mark out more than one choice in each section because both beliefs may be operating side by side.

Family beliefs
In my family:
Men are initiators and women are passive.
Women are initiators and men are passive.
Both sexes take equal responsibility for initiating sexual
    activity.

Men have much stronger sex drive than women.
Women have much stronger sex drive than men.
Men and women's sex drives are very similar.

Men mainly want sex and women mainly want love.

Men and women want sex and love in equal measures.

Men mainly want love and women mainly want sex.

Men are expected to have several sex relationships including extra-marital ones but women are expected to have few and to stay faithful.

Women are expected to have several sex relationships including extra-marital ones but men are expected to have few and to stay faithful.

Men are expected always to stay sexually faithful once married, as are women.

Both sexes are likely to have other sexual partners during marriage.

Infidelity is a hurdle to be got over.

Infidelity is grounds for immediate separation.

Infidelity is painful but can be dealt with provided it only happens once.

Women are expected to nurture men sexually but not to expect much sexual nurturing themselves.

Men are expected to take care of the woman's sexual needs regardless of their own.

Men and women should take equal responsibility for each other's sexual needs.

Men and women should take responsibility for their own sexual needs and expect the other to do so too.

Sex is mainly a physical outlet.
Sex is a comfort in times of anxiety.
Sex is an expression of love.
Sex is a method of domination.
Sex is mainly necessary for good health.
Sex is strictly for procreation.
Sex is an ecstatic, almost religious experience.
Sex is fun.

Good sex should be taken for granted.
Good sex needs constant care and work put in on it.
Good sex can only be spontaneous.

If you love each other everything will come right.
If something goes wrong sexually you should keep this
    private.
If something goes wrong sexually you should talk about it
    together.
If something goes wrong you should talk about it with a
    therapist.

It is wrong to tell children about sex.
It is wrong not to tell children about sex.
You should wait until a child reaches puberty before
    telling them about sex.

Nice people do not talk about sex openly.

Nice people talk about sex as freely as they do about
food.
Nice people should pick their moments to discuss
sexuality.
Nice people do not talk about sex to their parents.
Nice people do not talk about sex to their children.

> *The list could go on and on. I hope your family ethos
> becomes clearer after you have worked your way through
> these. By combining your ticked choices you can get a han-
> dle on what your family taught you about sex without your
> even knowing it.*

Peer-group beliefs

Among my friends I learned:
You should have as much sex as possible as soon as
possible.
You should save yourself till marriage.
You should wait for the right person, i.e. until you fall in
love, and only then have sex.

It is normal for boys to go through a homosexual phase.
It is normal for girls to go through a lesbian phase.
It is normal for girls and boys to pass through
homosexual phases on the way to heterosexuality.
It is normal for some boys and girls to remain either
homosexual, lesbian or bisexual.

It is abnormal for boys and girls to remain either
    homosexual, lesbian or bisexual.
It is abnormal for girls and boys to go through any phase
    other than that of developing heterosexuality.

It is normal to masturbate.
It is abnormal to masturbate.
Masturbation is OK provided it is seen as a phase to a
    more mature sexuality.
Masturbation is not OK if you are in a committed
    relationship.
Masturbation is great under any circumstances.

It is fun to look at pornography.
It is disgusting to look at pornography.
It's OK to look at pornography provided you do it with
    your committed partner.
Pornography is not OK in a committed relationship.
It is the individual's choice about whether or not they
    want to look at pornography and as such should not
    adversely affect a committed partner.

It is wrong to have sex anywhere other than in private.
It is fine to have sex at parties.
It is OK, in certain circumstances, to have sex in the same
    room as another couple.

It is fine to take part in different types of sex provided
    you do so only with other like-minded people.
It is healthy to enjoy sex in a threesome.
It is normal to go through a phase of swinging.
You will go to hell if you ever have sex with anyone other
    than your marital partner.
It is OK for other people to experience these alternative
    sexual activities but it is not for you.

It is fine to enjoy fetish sex either by yourself or with
    another provided you don't harm anyone.
It is reasonable to ask a partner to join you in a fetish
    activity.
It is not reasonable to pressurise a partner into fetish sex
    against their will.
An interest in fetish sex is the sign of a sick mind.
An interest in fetish sex is the mark of a progressive
    intelligence.

*If you have identified beliefs picked up from your friends,
take a further look at them and ask yourself whether these
are actually practical in your present life. Do they have real
meaning or are they based on superstition?*

Myths of sexuality
    *Read through the list and see if you can identify any that you
    believe in.*

Masturbation – the myths

1 Masturbation can make you blind.
2 It will make you ill, sap your energy.
3 It prevent you from being creative.
4 It is only practised by sad lonely people.
5 It will make you so addicted you will be unable to enjoy normal intercourse.
6 It is a sign of nymphomania.

Masturbation – the truths

1 Masturbation causes no physical harm at all unless it is done so roughly that you actually wound yourself.
2 It is a healthy, natural activity that, far from preventing creativity or sapping energy, probably relaxes the mind and body, giving you better physical conditions with which to work or play.
3 Masturbation actually provides the opportunity to explore and get familiar with your personal sexual response. Once you have managed this, it then allows you to take this knowledge into any subsequent relationship, thereby ensuring that the relationship has a greater likelihood of sexual success. It is, in this way, an excellent training and rehearsal for a sexual relationship.
4 Masturbation provides comfort and release for those without partners.
5 Masturbation is not addictive.

6   Although it is not a sign of nymphomania,
     masturbation may indicate a high sex drive.
7   Masturbation can be a fulfilling ecstatic experience in
     its own right.

Fantasy – the myths
A reliance on sexual fantasy is a sign of:
1   inadequacy;
2   inability to hold yourself in the here and now;
3   mental infidelity;
4   inability to experience pure sexual feeling for a
     partner;
5   a sick mind.

Fantasy – the truths
The ability to fantasise sexually:
1   is possibly the mark of a high testosterone count (for
     both males and females);
2   is indicative of a creative imagination;
3   cannot be policed because the imagination is beyond
     conscious control;
4   is probably a safeguard set up by the imagination to
     preserve long-term relationships when sex becomes
     repetitive;
5   may be a safeguard for bottled-up feelings and desires
     that would not be socially acceptable.

Male sex – the myths

Men must:

1 always be ready for sex;
2 be responsible for the woman's pleasure;
3 be hung like a bull to be sexually attractive;
4 always initiate, never be passive;
5 have dozens of sexual experiences;
6 always know what they are doing;
7 be in control.

Male sex – the facts

1 Men are entitled to their sexual moods just as women are. Men cannot usually be sexually aroused unless there is someone or something specific that is attractive.

2 Women need to be responsible for their own pleasure – not men, though it helps if men know what they are doing!

3 Penis size is irrelevant because it is what men do with their hands, mouth and entire body that counts to women. In a survey of what women find attractive in men, the great majority of men said they believed it was penis size that counted for women. Penis size however came virtually bottom of the list for the women. Instead they opted for buttocks as a source of visual turn-on.

4 According to women, some of the sexiest men are

	EVER READY	GIVES Pleasure	HUNG LIKE A 🛏️	ALWAYS ACTIVE	EXPERIENCE	KNOWS WHAT TO DO
DAVE	🧍🧍🧍	🧍	🧍	*(scribbled out)*	🧍🧍	🧍
TIM	🧍	🧍🧍	🧍🧍	*(scribbled out)*	🧍🧍🧍🧍	🧍🧍🧍
GEORGE	🧍🧍	🧍🧍🧍	🧍	*(scribbled out)*	🧍🧍🧍	🧍🧍
KOSTAS	🧍🧍🧍🧍	🧍🧍	🧍🧍🧍🧍	*(scribbled out)*	—	🧍🧍

those who feel sure enough about themselves to lie back and let the woman take charge.

5   Too much sexual experience can be both daunting and anxiety-making for some women who fear they a) will not measure up against an array of other sexual relationships and b) may contact the AIDS virus.

6   Spontaneity in sex is much prized.

7   A partner who is always in control leaves little room for spontaneity.

Female sex – the myths

Women:

1   must be passive for men to like and respect them;

2   should not show former knowledge of sexuality because that would make them appear 'bad';

3   should not ask for what they want in bed because that might make them sound demanding;

4   should wait for a man to express sexual interest before expressing any of their own;

5   find it hard to experience orgasm;

6   should possess perfect bodies to attract a man;

7   are nobody if they don't have a man;

8   should always please their man;

9   should fake orgasm if they can't actually experience one.

Female sex – the facts

1   Men usually love it when women take the sexual initiative.

2   Men enjoy their woman delighting them with some choice sex practice.

3   Women possess ordinary healthy sexual appetites as do men, and are equally entitled to make their own sexual experiments.

4   Women are responsible for their own sexuality.

5   Women need to know their own sexual response so that they can bring this information into a relationship and lift some of the pressure to succeed from men. Around 30 per cent of women experience orgasm during intercourse alone, but more than 80 per cent of women experience orgasm regularly through masturbation. Female orgasm usually needs a specific clitoral stimulation that intercourse alone often does not provide due to poor fit between male and female sexual anatomy. The majority of women can and do experience orgasm during intercourse provided they are stimulated by hand prior to intercourse and/or during intercourse.

6   Women are as attractive as they think they are, despite media stereotypes. Proof of this is in the numbers of fat, thin and elderly women who manage to have terrific sex lives.

7   Women in this day and age are finding more identity

from work and less identity from marriage.

8   It is good to please your lover but it is not always
possible.

9   The woman who fakes an orgasm does her love life a
disservice in the long-term because she is training her
lover to do sex the wrong way.

Orgasm – the myths

1   Orgasm must be experienced simultaneously.

2   If you don't experience orgasm you are inadequate.

3   If you don't provide your partner with an orgasm you
are inadequate.

4   A clitoral orgasm is inferior to a vaginal one.

5   Woman do not experience a proper orgasm since they
do not ejaculate.

6   Women cannot experience orgasm without foreplay.

7   You must have an orgasm.

8   The right way to have an orgasm is in the missionary
position.

9   A woman's genitals are ugly and so is her movement
during orgasm.

10 Orgasm means loss of control.

Orgasm – the facts

1   Orgasm can be experienced in any way, be it
separately or simultaneously. Many people say that
having to time an orgasm so that it exactly coincides

with that of a partner often detracts from the full orgasmic sensation.

2   There are many reasons for not experiencing orgasm and none of them has any bearing on an individual's self-worth.

3   Each of us is responsible for our own orgasm. This means that if your partner does not experience one it is up to him/her to improve things. Of course it would be great to help, but in the end, his/her climax is his/her responsibility.

4   There are many ways of experiencing climax, not only clitoral or vaginal, and no one way is any better or any worse than another.

5   Ejaculation is an old-fashioned definition of orgasm, especially since certain men climax without ejaculation and certain women with a very active G-spot appear to have an ejaculation.

6   Some women can climax by thought, i.e. fantasy alone. Some women can climax by intercourse alone. And others can climax the minute a partner penetrates them.

7   If orgasm becomes a must, the performance pressure this involves, works against you. There should be no compulsion on anyone to have an orgasm. Sometimes we just don't feel like it.

8   There is no 'right' way to have an orgasm. *Any way is the right way.*

9   Aesthetic taste is entirely personal. What is ugly to
    one individual is beautiful to another.
10 In one sense orgasm does mean a loss of control in
    that, at the moment of orgasm, we temporarily clock
    out to a different level of brain activity. But we never
    lose the ability to wrest ourselves straight back to
    earth if necessary – as may be witnessed in the case
    of young mothers with crying babies.

Problems and memes

Getting stuck in sex patterns during a long-term relationship

You've been married forever, you love each other but you
are uncomfortably aware that sex is now routine. Should
you try to change it? Or should you let well alone? Sex
works very well in this reliable pattern. But if you don't
change it, will your partner start to stray?

There is a lot of space given to research that shows that
men respond to novelty which is, clearly, impossible in a
well-established routine. In addition, men often experience
a mid-life crisis during their 40s when they suddenly pack
in the old wife and take up with a newer, younger one. In
contrast, there is also evidence which suggests that it is
normal to settle on a continuing sex pattern. But there is
absolutely no evidence to show that suddenly dressing up

in black underwear and a mask makes the slightest difference to saving a marriage. If the marriage is going to continue, it is as likely to do so still using the same sex routine as not.

There might be good reason, however, for looking at the emotion underlying the marriage. Clair Hawes, a clinical psychologist from Vancouver, suggests improving the quality of a long-term relationship by concentrating on the small things that give it meaning. She suggests taking a look at some key areas around sexual intercourse, which you might be able to strengthen and improve. These are:

- sensitivity to each other's mood during intercourse;
- carving out private time for intimacy;
- deliberately giving each other's body more loving stimulation, possibly in the shape of a sensual massage;
- making a point of giving much greater stimulation to the genitals on the grounds that ageing can mean diminished sexual sensation;
- deliberately putting yourself in the way of sexual stimulation, such as sexy books or films which you can watch from your bed;
- making love occasionally at times other than the usual ones;
- taking a lot more holidays together. The break in routine can be stimulating.

MY MEME SUGGESTION Appreciate the exact routine that has worked so well for you during the years and trust it. It is *your* routine. It works for you. If your relationship is really in danger, the dangers will be focused on issues other than sex. Have faith in your idea of good sex. But don't be afraid to talk about the feelings underneath it.

Wanting less sex than your partner does

The trouble with one person not wanting as much sex as the other is that the other is constantly put into a role of begging and pleading. The supplicant begins to feel unloved, unattractive, angry and restless.

There's a variety of ways to work on this one.

- If the less sexually active partner is willing s/he might start using testosterone gel, rubbing it in to the skin on a regular basis. This stimulates sex drive, arousal and sensitivity.

- If the problem has arisen because the withholding partner is feeling steamrollered by their partner's needs, then a sex contract is useful. In this you might mutually agree to him choosing for three nights of the week, her choosing for three nights of the week, leaving the seventh night up for grabs.

- If the unwilling partner is bored, either by the sex or by the relationship, this needs time spent on talking. Can you make interesting enough conversation to rejuvenate sexual interest? Or can you decide to part

on the grounds that you can't manage to sustain a life with little or no sex?

MY MEME SUGGESTION Accept the situation at its face value, i.e. that your partner still loves you but, for reasons of his/her own, doesn't feel terribly sexual. But be aware yourself and warn him/her that this means that since you are responsible for your own sex life you are therefore making the choice to sexually satisfy yourself in other ways. This may mean using methods of masturbation, by enjoying sexual relationships outside your committed relationship, or by simply getting so much hugging and cuddling from your committed partner that it largely makes up for the lessened penis/vagina contact.

In case you doubt the possibility of surviving a marriage where sex is almost or completely gone, remind yourself that your doubts are based on a meme – the one that says you can't have marriage without sex. You can, and many do, who continue to love each other dearly enough to be able to give each other the freedom to be sexual in other ways.

Not wanting any sex at all

This is an extended version of the previous problem.

If you both regret the plight of your love life, a medical examination might be in order. Viagra might be a solution for a man, or vacuum methods of sustaining an erection, or cutting down on the booze (alcohol creates impotence). If you are a female, take a look at what is happening to your hormones. Hormone replacement might help.

If neither of you cares much about the continuity of sex, don't give it another thought. If you can manage to be happy without sex, good luck to you. You don't have a problem. But if one of you resents the situation, take a look at the answer to the previous question, including my meme suggestion.

Getting inhibited because you think you ought to be doing sex better

A typical example of this is the woman who believes she is spoiling her husband's enjoyment of sex because she isn't having orgasms. The more she tries to have orgasms under these conditions, the less likely it is that she will experience them. The more she attempts to loosen up her behaviour, the more threatening this will feel and the more inhibited she will become.

There are two areas to look at here. The easiest is to overcome the inhibition. If the couple works on giving each other sensual massage with intercourse forbidden, they can learn to progress to highly erotic massage in unpressurised circumstances. By doing this they may be able to educate themselves more accurately than they have previously managed about what it takes to get the woman to orgasm. By combining the stimulus of erotic books or films with self-massage they may be able to heighten the erotic atmosphere enough. Alternatively, this may be something the woman wants to do on her own in a programme of self-stimulation and self-exploration. (See the appendix for suitable training books.)

The second area is the reason the woman is feeling such anxiety in the first place. If her anxieties are based on complaints of her husband's, the problem may not be hers at all. It may instead belong to the husband. Some men feel inadequate sexually and displace their feelings on to their wife. Professional counselling may help to improve this.

MY MEME SUGGESTION Tell yourself that each one of us is responsible for our own orgasm. This means that if one person wants something improved it is up to that individual to improve it – not the partner. On a purely practical level this means that the dissatisfied partner needs to take a look at his own dissatisfaction. He is, after all, managing to experience an orgasm. So what is it that doesn't work for him? If he is anxious about his skills as a lover, perhaps that ought to be the focus of marital counselling. If he has deep-seated anxieties about his effectiveness in the world, he needs to take a look at them. He needs to be stopped from dumping his anxieties on his partner – they do not belong to her.

CASE HISTORY

Anthony complained about his wife's lack of orgasm to the therapist, describing her as frigid. Julia subsequently worked with the therapist on learning to give herself an orgasm and managed it, without too much difficulty. It then became obvious that Anthony was a very poor lover who had never taken the trouble to stimulate his wife at all. When Julia went back into the relationship saying, 'Look, isn't it marvellous, I can climax. Let's do it together,' Anthony became impotent. He had felt powerful thanks to his assumed superiority. When he felt that superiority had been taken away from him, he felt threatened.

Finding it very hard to start a sexual relationship because you feel the other person is expecting great things of you and you know that you take your time in coming to the boil

This is an anxiety based on a belief about yourself. This belief tells you that you have to be a perfect lover who can make no mistakes and that if you cannot live up to this then you are a failure as a person. You will be unable to hold on to a partner because you won't be attractive enough to retain his/her interest. And since you know it takes time for you to get to trust someone and therefore

really to let go sexually in their presence, you despair in advance.

Some of the messages of assertion training come in useful here. One of them is: 'It is OK to make mistakes but it's a good idea if you can learn from them.' The whole point about mistakes is that they are half of a learning process. The other half is what you do with them. So next time you meet a potential lover, explain at some appropriate stage that you need to take things slowly. Reveal that you get nervous because you fear too much will be expected of you. If you feel things going too fast, don't hesitate to roll away. If your new partner moves too rapidly towards intercourse, pull back. Say, 'I really want to do this but I don't feel right about it yet.'

Thirty years of having a sex life has taught me that if your new partner is the 'right' one s/he will understand and cope well, things will improve and you won't compromise or freeze in fear. If your new partner is the wrong one, s/he won't have the patience to deal with your hesitations and you will have learned something valuable about him/her. If s/he can't be patient right at the start of things, s/he will be even less likely to be patient at any later stage.

MY MEME SUGGESTION Recognise that the reason we persist with new partners who we fear may not be quite right is because we fear we will never find one who is. Learn to recognise and trust your instincts here. Don't ditch people before you give them a chance to unwind; after all they may have the same difficulty that you do. Please do give them time. But learn to feel good about yourself and your ability to survive without a partner in the world if needs be. It is usually only when we have gained this kind of strength and independence that we become truly attractive. A common meme is we cannot live without another to love us. While it is certainly true that it is much more pleasurable to love and be loved, you can also live perfectly happily without this. So reassemble your thoughts with regard to your own inner strengths.

Feeling inferior because your idea of sex isn't doing it on a saturday night in the marital bed in the missionary position
You are probably one of those lucky people with an effortless sexuality. It takes very little to make you come to orgasm. Which means that you really adore going to that occasional 'special' party. You actually have experimented with threesomes and swinging and lived to enjoy the experiences. But, and it's a big but, you are forced to keep completely quiet about your sexuality. You are quite sure that if you let on in any way about your sexual adventures you will end up an outcast, on the edge of society. And this has repercussions for married life. It is almost impossible to settle down to the cosy routine of sex on a Saturday night because you go mad with boredom and frustration. But

you are a human being and you do want to settle down. So you feel very unhappy with yourself. You believe there is something intrinsically dirty about you and that you will never be good enough to deserve a regular marriage.

This a heavy trip to carry. You are presumably one of those people who is bold in bed but shy about expressing your independence of thought to a partner. Your instinct in not doing so may be entirely appropriate. But if a major force in your life has to be permanently hidden it is indeed going to be difficult to find the right person to attach yourself to. First of all you must stop feeling inferior. You are as good and as valuable as anyone else. In some ways you are blessed. There are great advantages to possessing an 'effortless sexuality'. You can be completely confident about this part of your being – many others are not.

Your sexuality is part of the normal range of human sexual response and there is nothing wrong or 'dirty' about it or you. Your real problem is other people's judgemental attitudes about your sexual behaviour. You don't want to be an outcast so how exactly do you proceed? The answer would be to build on that 'easy sexuality' rather than shovel it under the carpet. The partner most likely to accept and appreciate you would be someone with a similar approach to life. So make relationships with those people you meet at sex parties and give them the chance to continue outside the party. Start looking for emotional depths as well as sexual ones. Once you meet someone who can accept you, sexuality and all, you will start feeling much better about yourself.

MY MEME SUGGESTION Take a look at the prejudiced attitudes that say sex variations are wrong. See them for the mark of ignorance and fear they are. When someone attacks it is because s/he feels seriously threatened. There's no point in going around threatening people in turn. Instead pay them the respect of letting them hang on to their ideas and learn to be strong about your own. Yours are based on the knowledge that you are a perfectly decent human being. So every time you get that inferior feeling back tell yourself it is someone else's fear that is trying to control you.

Feeling inferior because your idea of sex is doing it on saturday night in the marital bed in the missionary position
Every magazine that you pick up has an article on how to do sex in 69 different positions. And you really don't like this. It's not that you begrudge other people hanging from a chandelier. But you are getting to feel really inadequate because you never want to swing yourself. You enjoy sex all right. In its proper place. So how do you prevent yourself from feeling like someone's great-great-grandmother?

You can take comfort from the fact that, although a lot is written about the newer raunchier sex lives of men and

complicated

women, statistics and anecdotal evidence both show that there's a big gap between the articles and real life.

MY MEME SUGGESTION Next time you have a tinge of anxiety, remind yourself that most possible partners are likely to be highly relieved that you will settle for something regular but good. People like you are in the majority so forget the publicity and look forward to Saturday night! If you want to make it special give your partner a massage as a little extra. This is the friendliest, most sensual gift you can offer anyone. But if you really don't want to do that, don't. You are entitled to your preferences.

You don't feel very satisfied by your orgasm. You are glad to have one at all but it seems short and slight. Why can't it be earth-shattering like in the romantic novels?

Orgasm is immensely variable. Not only does it vary from person to person but it also varies on nearly every occasion an individual experiences it. If you haven't experienced an orgasm for a long time, when it arrives it may be pent-up, explosive, strong, urgent and full of sharp sensation. If this is your fifth orgasm of the day, it may be difficult to attain, short, slight, with little or muted sensation. Orgasm can go on for hours or it can last for a couple of seconds. Some people do not feel the sensation of their orgasm at all and only know it is happening because they feel the movement or watch the movement in a mirror – a kind of anaesthetised orgasm. Verbal descriptions of orgasm vary from 'it's like the gentle rippling of waves' to 'it's a piercing sensation that spreads deeper and deeper until my whole body is sharp with amazing feeling'.

So why don't you experience something deeper? Here's a list of reasons.

- You are not getting long enough erotic build-up in advance. You need tons more foreplay that is delayed and delayed and delayed.
- If you are female, perhaps your partner is stopping stimulating you the minute your orgasm begins. Women differ slightly from men in that the clitoral stimulation must continue if the sensation is to last for as long as possible. Once it stops, so does the climax.
- You are so busy trying to control the orgasm that you and your body don't let go enough for the climax to feel really wild. You could try working on letting go. Try beating cushions, screaming, crying, gasping, shouting, especially when you feel yourself getting near to climax.
- You've been having too much sex and each subsequent climax is harder to achieve and the sensation is diminished. Lay off for a while and see

what happens.

- If you are female, perhaps your hormone system is naturally a little short of free-ranging testosterone – the hormone that influences libido, desire and sensation. Try to find a specialist in sexual medicine who will assess your testosterone levels and, if appropriate, prescribe testosterone gel.

- If you are male and little or no sensation has always been the case you may be suffering from insufficient testosterone or you may have some hang-ups that are affecting your mind control. The best way to sort this out is to get the various tests that tell you about the state of your hormone system.

- Unless your orgasm is so slight as to be hardly felt, I would suggest you examine the relationship in which you are experiencing this difficulty. If the difficulty is with yourself, then you may need some medical assistance, but if it is only within the relationship that orgasm feels so unsatisfactory and if orgasm works fine during masturbation, then take a look at your feelings about exposing yourself sexually to this particular partner. Is it him/her particularly? Or is with any partner that this happens? It could be that you are suffering from one of the inhibition problems I mentioned in chapter 2. You could work on these inhibitions with a therapist, this could help you change some of the fixed ideas that are holding you back. Or if this doesn't work, you could try specific medication.

MY MEME SUGGESTION If none of these succeeds, work on appreciating what you have got instead of lamenting what you don't have.

You would like to experience orgasm every time you make love but this doesn't always happen. does this mean that something is wrong?

Not at all. Desire is as variable as the quality of orgasm. There are times when we make love only because our partner wants it. Even though we don't particularly feel like it we go ahead because we love them. Sometimes there are other things on our mind that rob us of the ability fully to let go.

But it is important to explain why this has happened in such a way that your lover does not feel rejected. If, however, your lack of orgasm is becoming more and more frequent, then you need to take a look at yourself and how you are feeling about the relationship. What is happening to you or between you that seems to be putting orgasm out of the question?

MY MEME SUGGESTION Why should you experience orgasm every time you have sex? Who says you should? *There is*

no correct way in which to have sex. Of course it is pleas-
ant to experience orgasm. But only if you really desire it.
Desire is the crux – not orgasm. Nor is desire the only cri-
terion. If you don't desperately desire someone sexually, it
does not mean you don't love them. But it might mean that
your relationship is changing in some way that needs to be
acknowledged, if only by you.

A new source of sexual love patterns

Heterosexuals are usually so busy feeling superior they do
not imagine they could learn from other groups of
humans, and the last thing they would do is take a few tips
from animals. That thought is abhorrent, which is a pity
because men and women could learn something if they
dared to let go of the insecurities on which their prejudices
are founded.

Masters and Johnson, the US sex researchers, found
during their work on homosexual couples that gay and lesbian patterns of love making differed quite a bit from those
of heterosexuals. When they launched their book *Homosexuality in Perspective*, one of the publicity points much
featured in the media was that the great sexologists considered heterosexual men and women could learn from
homosexual love-making patterns. Gay men, it emerged in
the research, spent far more time on foreplay, exhibited
more tenderness, and were happy to reach climax in many
ways other than intercourse. Some couples would spend

hours stroking each other and building up sexual excitement with the thought of finishing the session (as in climax), far from their minds. Love-making was a whole-body experience and orgasm only a final part of it.

Tips to follow
- Make love without orgasm.
- Spend a two-hour period on massage alone.
- Practise stroking only certain limbs but stroke them often.
- Think whole body.
- Forget the genitals – they will manage to take care of themselves in the fullness of time.
- Curb impatience – impatience simply means that your mind is somewhere else and that you probably shouldn't be love-making at all right now.

As for the animals
A fascinating book by Bruce Bagemihl, *Animal Diversity*, was published in 1999. In it the author documented the fact that, despite popular belief, almost all animals exhibit homosexual behaviour. Much of this is specifically genitally oriented but not all. For example, Bagemihl poetically describes the twining and intertwining of those long graceful necks of male giraffes, snaking and undulating around each other's skin. What he describes, though it may lead to sexual behaviour, is a type of sensuality. Since

giraffes cannot be said to possess a higher consciousness it could reasonably be argued that these animals are innocents. What happens innocently is not wrong. Human sensuality is not wrong either. When a little child unconsciously strokes its parent's arm, enjoying the pure sensation of the stroke, this is innocence. Our great sadness is that thanks to the layers of civilisation heaped on us by our 'intelligence', we lose this direct ability to communicate by sensual touch.

Hugging for health

As 'grown-ups' we can't turn back the clock. We can't lose that conscious 'knowledge' of what is considered sexually right or wrong. But we can try to set aside some prejudices and allow ourselves to be physically warmer, stroking dear friends of either sex. Men and women adore being touched. They react to caresses with feelings of powerful friendship. If you go out and hug a friend, it does not automatically mean that the friend receives the 'wrong idea'. Any idea that springs into their head will be partially dictated by your own attitude. If your attitude is that touch is a great way of conveying friendship but that is all, then that is what will come across. And if your friend resists this boundary, explain your philosophy. In the 1970s there was a great touchy-feely movement emanating from California: Give A Friend A Hug Day was seriously celebrated. The most unlikely individuals found

themselves in warm embrace. College professors, businessmen and politicians all managed it. And for a few seconds they enjoyed this rare contact.

So the message from the animals is to keep cuddling. The sensuality of cuddling does not have to be sexual. But it can feed all kinds of other emotional needs. You and your mates are likely to feel a lot better after a non-sexual cuddle. So risk trying it out. And watch what happens. If nothing else, life feels more satisfactory.

Sex ideas through time

Every couple of generations the way in which we experience sex changes. There may not be a change in what actually happens – penis still goes into vagina – but there is a difference in how sex is seen and valued as an intrinsic part of life. Through thinking differently and through shifting attitudes, the experience imperceptibly alters. The computer generation, for example, used to taking on board short but sharp bursts of information, may need to experience sex much more hurriedly than former generations. We know this is already happening where reading is concerned. Concentration spans seem to be shortening but they are also becoming more intense.

So in this chapter we take a look at who we are sexually, bearing in mind that *who we are depends on when we are*. Our survey is limited to a little over 100 years because it is only in the late nineteenth century that written records of sexual activities began to be kept. But we want to know about the sexual attitudes of our grandparents and great-grandparents because it is these that form the building blocks of our sexual attitudes.

On the foundations of our grandparents' beliefs we

build, renovate and recreate. We inherit some of their ideas and ways of being. But ways of thinking and being also evolve during our own time, thanks to the horizontal transmission of memes – the situation where we get ideas from our peers, rather than solely from parents. It can be a fascinating exercise to look back over the past century or so and work out what we may have taken on from our near ancestors and what we bring from our present-day culture.

The late 1800s to the early 1900s – the double standards

Undoubtedly, many fortunate men and women of the Victorian era hit upon good sexual experience by happy accident, in the same way as some people do today. But the overriding belief of Victorian men and women of the middle class was that sex was not something nice respectable women enjoyed. This was after all the age of such sexual repression that even the legs of chairs were covered up. Middle-class women expected little in the shape of sexual ecstasy. Indeed, they probably feared sexual encounters at the start of marriage and may have lived stoically without ever experiencing sexual pleasure.

Since contraception was virtually non-existent and little known about, women would have been desperate not to have sex so often. For working-class women in particular, having sex also meant another agonising experience of

childbirth, another mouth to feed, even more exhaustion and yet more pressure.

The double standard of the time held that men had uncontrollable sexual appetites which had to be slaked for reasons of health. If you were middle class, this meant you sought sex with someone other than your nicely brought-up wife. In late-Victorian times there were hundreds of thousands of prostitutes – women and children of both sexes. There were brothels in all major cities, patronised by men who thought it normal to enjoy this secret life. So enjoyable sex was something to hide, to be swept under the carpet.

Masturbation was considered physically harmful; every teaspoon of semen was believed to equal the loss of a pint of blood. Appalling contraptions were invented to prevent the inveterate masturbator from having his wicked way with himself (and it would have been a 'him' – for a woman to have given herself pleasure in this way would have been unthinkable).

WHAT MIGHT WE HAVE INHERITED FROM THIS? The notions that sex:
- is dirty;
- should be hidden and never talked about;
- is only really enjoyable when done under 'forbidden' conditions;
- is only really enjoyable when exploiting the vulnerable;

- is a source of stress and conflict, misery and pain;
- is fine for men but out of the question for women;
- can be responsible for poverty and starvation;
- in the shape of masturbation, is physically harmful.

The work and translations by the great Victorian explorer Sir Richard Burton were among the few liberal features of the late 1800s. Burton and his wife Isabel travelled extensively in Arabia and the Far East. Burton became fascinated by the ancient collections of erotic writing that he stumbled across. He commissioned English-speakers among the native men to translate some of the books and published them by private subscription in England. He was so aware of the opprobrium he would generate by doing this that he chose to remain anonymous with the publication of the first book, the *Kama Sutra*. Word quickly got out, however, and he didn't bother to safeguard anonymity with the publication of the next two, *The Perfumed Garden* and *The Ananga Ranga*. Although these were still most decidedly regarded as 'dirty books' they possessed a certain cachet, if only because Burton himself was a commanding figure and did eventually talk about them openly.

WHAT MIGHT WE HAVE INHERITED FROM THIS? The notions that sex might also:
- be exotic;
- be a suitable interest for certain intellectuals and

chemise cagoule

hole

FRONT

BACK

with spikes

members of the upper classes only, provided that they
were male;
* supply information about a variety of sex positions
and their particular strengths and weaknesses, about
matters of sexual etiquette and hygiene.

The 1920s and the 1930s – taking it to the priest

Throughout the nineteenth and the early twentieth centuries there was a terrific rise in the power and role of the
church. Thousands of churches were built and, thanks to
the social life that revolved around them, they were well
attended. The priest or vicar was someone to turn to in a
time of trouble. Thanks to the devastation of the First
World War (1914–18) many social institutions and barri-
ers broke down or dissolved and among these, to some
degree, went the inhibition of talking about sex.

It was during this period that the ideas of Freud, Jung
and Adler began to reach a wider public. With this background came more conversation about sex and the breaking down of social taboos – more and more men and
women felt able to talk about their sexual problems. But
not with each other. And this is where the priest or vicar
came in. Even when men and women visited the priest for
help, they didn't admit to having a sex problem. Their language was voiced in terms of faith. They presented their
problems as spiritual ones.

MARIE STOPES' POST BAG

Seeking spiritual help was particularly common among women. Marie Stopes, the British sexual and contraceptive reformer, received sackfuls of letters from distressed females after the publication of her highly controversial book *Married Love*. In these letters they regularly complained that they had consulted the priest or vicar about their pain or lack of enjoyment in the nuptial bed. By sorting out their spiritual life, they were told, they would become easier and happier within themselves and their sexuality would be that much more likely to flow smoothly. In the sense that this is a forerunner of psychosexual counselling, there is truth in this. However, practical help in the shape of physical work and medical intervention was still a long way off. Stopes' letters told of truly bleak marriages. In the US Margaret Sanger did similar pioneering work on sexual reforms such as birth control.

It's important to make clear that up until this point most 'nicely brought-up' women and many men simply knew nothing about sex. They didn't know how it worked; they knew nothing about female orgasm; they probably believed masturbation was harmful; there was an abyss of sexual ignorance. Growing out of the now increased discussion of sexuality came an awareness of the appalling conditions of working-class people burdened with enormous families. Marie Stopes and others began to set up the first birth-control clinics to make contraception widely available and not a luxury for those with money.

WHAT MIGHT WE HAVE INHERITED FROM THIS? The notions that sex can be:
- talked about;
- controlled;
- understood;
- enjoyed by women if they have the right background;

We might also have learned that the role of church ministers included some teaching and education about sex on the basis of faith and Christianity.

The 1940s and 1950s – sex becomes medicalised

Thanks to the growing availability of birth control for women, sex began slowly to become medicalised. During the Second World War (1939–45), due to the careful priority given to the forces with regard to controlling venereal disease, men had been able to talk to their medical officer about sexual problems. Once the war was over, women began to talk to their doctors about birth control and gynaecological problems – but not about what actually happened between man and woman in bed.

Since the help available was confined to health matters, this meant that physical health improved but the nitty-gritty of what went on between the sheets did not. Nice men and women still did not talk openly about sex, thanks to their Victorian inheritance. So there were still a lot of misconceptions. Women, because they were not capable of ejaculation, were generally believed to have no equivalent sexual response to that of men. Many doctors believed (and continued to do so until the 1980s) that, because of this, women did not climax or at least experienced only an incomplete and inferior orgasm. This meant that men could feel supremely confident about their own sexual performance but often, unfortunately, at the expense of their partner.

WHAT MIGHT WE HAVE INHERITED FROM THIS? The notions that:

- sex is a medical issue but still not to be talked about outside the marriage bed;
- women are sexually inferior to men and unlikely to have any kind of equivalent response;
- men must be responsible for women's lesser sexuality;
- women must be shown what to do.

The 1960s to the 1980s – taking it to the relationship counsellor

This was an era of flowering sexual research. Thanks to

the pioneering work done by Alfred Kinsey and Masters and Johnson in the 1940s and 1950s, the new information filtered through to the general public slowly but surely during the 1960s and 1970s. Men and women learned that major changes were possible in their most intimate lives.

Men learned that they might control certain sex problems to some extent instead of feeling helpless about them. Women learned that not only were they *not* sexually inferior but that, thanks to multiple orgasm, they might even be superior. Suddenly orgasm for everyone became a possibility. And there was the bonus that everyone talked about it. But now different pressures settled on male and female shoulders. Men complained that women were too demanding. Thanks to the growth of feminism and the relative safety of the contraceptive pill, women were suddenly unafraid to ask for more satisfactory sex and were no longer prepared to put up with poor quality. This put huge pressures on to men. The relationship between the sexes became *over*-sexualised. You were supposed to have sex frequently in the name of normality.

Since having great sex all the time was easier said than done, people began to need a lot of reassurance. The relationship counsellor was invented and instead of continuing to go to the priest with your spiritual dilemma, you went to the therapist with your sexual dilemma.

WHAT MIGHT WE HAVE INHERITED FROM THIS? We may believe that:

- a good sex life is everyone's right and that we can all expect to enjoy a lot of orgasms in our time;
- women can be as dynamic in bed as men and this is normal – it doesn't mean that they are somehow 'bad' people;
- thanks to effective birth control we no longer need to choose sexual relationships so carefully since we are unlikely to bear babies as a result. Recreational sex can be one of our pastimes.

The 1990s – a swing to the pharmaceutical

By the end of the 1990s a great deal of work had been carried out on the physiology of sex – how sex actually works. While during the 1970s, 90 per cent of sex problems were considered to be all in the mind, now the balance swung to the belief that at least 66 per cent of sex problems were caused by physical dilemmas. All that was needed was to pop a pill and – hey presto, off you go again. Human beings learned how to chemically modify their ability to function. And went to considerable expense in order to do so. But by now the hype about sex had become so extreme that another belief emerged – if you didn't enjoy sex you were not a functioning modern being. It thus became imperative that sex worked and was seen to work. This

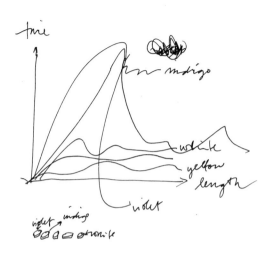

true

indigo

white

yellow

length

violet

violet → indigo

chromile

was in spite of pretty consistent surveys which showed that up to half of men and women having regular sex considered that there was something unsatisfactory about it. This probably indicates that it is normal for sex to vary enormously in quality.

WHAT MIGHT WE HAVE INHERITED FROM THIS? Many people believe now that:

- sex works mechanically;
- you can have ultimate control over sex;
- you should be able to have sex with anyone and enjoy it;
- you can fix anything.

The turn of the millennium

Drugs continue to be an overriding interest with longevity drugs keeping people younger and testosterone gel endowing men and women with a prolonged ability to feel and respond sexually. But the scientific emphasis is shifting gradually to understanding how the brain works. It is no accident that this book is written with a background of evolutionary psychology, in particular exploring how our brains function and how we may or may not be able to programme our little grey cells. On the basis of a greater understanding of how the brain controls the body we may come to think differently (alternatively) about sex. One observation about the role of testosterone in sexual function has been to make a connection between increased sexuality and enhanced imagination. It would be interesting if, on this basis, creativity turned out to be irrevocably linked with sexual dynamism. In the next chapter I talk about possible connections between the two and how we may bring creativity into day-to-day sexual fun.

After rereading this chapter you may perceive that many of the beliefs we have inherited from our forebears are in conflict with each other. Most of us believe both the old ideas and the new ones. We can probably see, with all our considerable acuity, that one custom makes a great deal of sense and yet, for some intangible reason, we cannot subscribe to it. What holds us back? Almost certainly it is great-grandmother, lodged defiantly inside our twenty-first century brain. Take just one contemporary belief – that we ought to be able to let go and enjoy ourselves sexually with any halfway suitable partner. Our inner great-grandmother will tell us that we are immoral creatures for wanting to do this, that we somehow defile ourselves, and even though we now think this is rubbish, the idea is there, inside, directing the traffic of our thoughts.

It also gets clearer as we look back that many of the beliefs were erroneous in the first place. This means it is perfectly possible that we, in the here and now, are still functioning on misbelief. It's another reason why we need to look deeper into our murky sexual psyches.

How can you identify the sexual beliefs of your own family?

It helps to have living elderly relatives to whom you can talk. Contrary to what you might expect, many of these elders are interested in looking back and talking about how they themselves lived their lives.

> QUESTIONS FOR ELDERLY RELATIVES
> What was the relationship between your parents like?
> What religious beliefs might have directed you?
> What social background did you emerge from and how might this have impacted on your beliefs?
> What were the circumstances of your early life? Did you grow up in times of peace or of war?
> Were you rich or poor?
> Did your parents seem loving towards each other?
> How many children did you have?
> Did you yourself ever suffer from repressive social attitudes about sex?
> Did you have an enjoyable physical relationship with your own partner or were there difficulties?

Without being overly prurient you can garner a surprising amount of information, which gives a good idea of how your near ancestors lived their sexual lives. Look out for dramatic incidents such as unwed parenthood, rejection by

parents, a secret abortion, a jilted or jilting lover, an alco-
holic who sexually terrorised his/her partner, a war-time
disability that affected a sex life – the list is endless. These
are all events that will in some tiny way impact on your
own life today. Now make a list of your own sexual beliefs
and see if you can link any of these with the events you
have researched.

The family constellation
Another exercise, borrowed from Adlerian psychology, is
to picture your family as a constellation of stars. See yourself as the sun, the biggest brightest star, and place each
member of your family either near or far, depending on
what you feel is the extent of their influence on you. When
you have drawn up your constellation, take a look at the
characters closest and think about the sexual example that
they may have provided. What might you have unconsciously learned from these emotionally close relatives
about sensuality?

How else might you identify the way in which you
yourself are likely to approach sexuality, and sexual problems in particular? Try thinking back to your earliest childhood. Remember the earliest incident regarding sexuality
that comes to mind. Picture this incident as a scene in a
film. Now freeze the frame of the film so that you are looking at a static picture. What title would you give the picture? And what feelings does this special scene evoke?

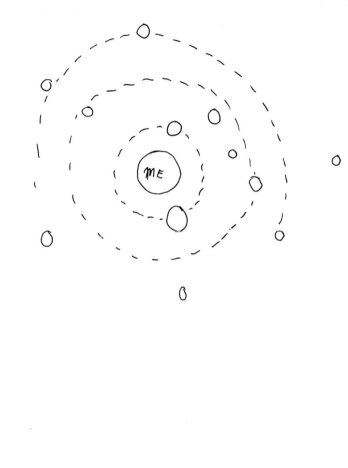

ANNA'S EXAMPLE

FILM SCENE 'One of my earliest memories is of playing sex games with another little girl at about the age of eight. The door to our room opens and in comes my grandmother who is not pleased to find out what we are doing. After this, the little girl and I are not allowed to play with each other any more and although I didn't feel at the time as if I were doing anything wrong, now I feel guilty. Somehow, unknowingly, I was bad.'

SNAPSHOT 'I am halted mid game, with my grandmother's face peering round the door.'

TITLE OF SNAPSHOT Bad girls

FEELINGS 'I've disgraced myself but I don't know why.'

POSSIBLE IMPACT ON FUTURE It may be hard for Anna to trust either her own feelings or those of a new partner since the awful underlying thought exists that she might be disgracing herself all over again. Alternatively, she might be so angry about feeling guilty that she becomes defiant. Her reaction therefore might be to become blatantly and defiantly sexual. This is not to say that any of these feelings work at a conscious level, but they may underpin everything about her sex life at an unconscious level.

If underlying feelings about sex are unconscious, you might wonder why we bother to find out what they are. The reason for doing so is that by becoming aware of unconscious motivation it brings your actions and behaviour into the conscious. You can then choose to alter your sexual behaviour if that is what you prefer. Or you can continue to sin with impunity!

These methods work even more effectively when both members of a couple identify their unconscious feelings about sex and then compare notes. Anna found that her partner's feelings led him to be assertive about the way in which he carried out his sex life. She loved this because his ready expectation that any sex was good sex overcame her small feelings of guilt. It also suited the defiant aspect of her character in that it allowed her to be more sexual than her inner great-grandmother would have liked.

Sex as creativity

The link between sex and creativity is energy. One of the early explanations of the creation of the world put it that the world was the result of a cataclysmic orgasm of the gods – a fusion of sex and energy. Yet in all the subjective descriptions of sexuality we are currently presented with, little attention has been paid to the fact that, even not counting conception, the sex act is an intensely creative event. It is perhaps one of the most creative actions that human beings ever take.

When we begin having sex we don't actually know how to do it. We understand the functions but we don't know how to do the feelings, the approaches, the when and where to lay hands. We do not usually have other people to set us an example or teach us. We are forced to come up with a way of doing sex *all by ourselves,* a way uniquely and creatively our own. It is particularly creative because it is an invention of not one but two people and as such the permutations are multiplied – there may be many wonderful variations of such an invention. And for ever afterwards it remains creative because every experience of sex is a new experience. Each time we do sex we are a day older, we think differently, we move differently, we bring a different mood to our coupling.

Freud's legacy

Sex has been linked to many sorts of creativity other than the sex act – but often in a negative way. One of Freud's legacies has been to see sex as a cause of envy, a reason for sublimation, a target for repression, though not all of the blame should be laid at his door. Freud was probably only echoing the sexual sentiments of his time. As a result writers, artists, philosophers – anyone making any kind of creative movement in their life – were thought to be either:

- compensating for some lack they felt (left over from childhood);
- defending themselves from something bad, either real or imagined;
- rewarding themselves in fantasy because real life is ultimately not rewarding;
- sublimating infantile sexuality.

Possibly all of these suggestions regarding creativity are true. Yet they are only a part of the picture. It is like observing that the glass is half empty. If you take the view that the glass is half full, you start to see that there are many highly positive links between creativity and sex as well.

When sex involves play

Sexual creativity comes in many forms. One form is play. People play. They play at all stages of their life and they particularly play in bed. Play is valuable in evolutionary survival but there is disagreement in understanding the value of this. One argument has it that play allows you to rehearse situations. Other thinkers have pointed out that it is not necessary to play in order to rehearse. Yet another argument has it that play is a simple physical release of energy, but there are many ways to release energy without involving the fun aspect.

Watching animals at play you can see the difference between play behaviour and serious behaviour. According to psychiatrist Anthony Storr, play behaviour is exaggerated and uneconomical. The motor patterns used in play are those which the animals might use in serious situations but they are used in the wrong order, or done incompletely, or repeated over and over again, or exaggerated so that they are inefficient. And it's the same with humans. What's more, higher animals such as the primates, most especially the chimpanzee, can extend play to such skills as painting pictures with oil paints. According to zoologist Desmond Morris, chimpanzees become so absorbed in painting that they sometimes have tantrums when they are stopped. They may prefer painting to feeding and as a result get caught up in what he calls 'self-rewarding activities'. Most aspects of sex are also self-rewarding – I doubt if there are many individuals who only do sex for the sake of others.

And of course we play during sex. We endlessly create and recreate our expressions of love and sensuality. We reward our partners by doing so. We reward ourselves. Writing a book is tangible evidence of creative play; the sense of connection between lovers is intangible evidence.

Sexual creativity and 'survival'

Desmond Morris considers play to be an 'extra', something done for its own sake. Yet the human being who can play and be creative in entertaining a mate, may pull in a better mate than the human who can not. Play (and the arts linked with play) may well give us evolutionary survival advantages.

But what about survival in the here and now? The most obvious advantage to sexual play and to the creative arts is that both safeguard against boredom. If you think that boredom is irrelevant to survival please think again. Emotional survival in human beings is almost as important as physical survival.

Morris explains that there is a physical underpinning for such a notion. He says man and the higher primates belong to a category of animal that requires constant stimulation if the nervous system is to function at its most efficient. If there isn't any immediate stimulation from the surroundings then the creature or human will seek out something or invent it. It sounds as if in order to continue 'being' we have to continue 'doing' or, at the very least, 'experiencing', even if it is at second-hand. To term experiences gained through art as 'second-hand' is a misnomer however. We only ever experience life through the medium of our own brain. Any experience in the brain therefore is of direct value.

If we bring these ideas back to sex and if we return to some of Freud's premises, it becomes apparent that sexual play is not an infantile approach, a rehearsal or a method of learning. Taken to its heights, sex can be viewed as the ultimate projection of pure self – a true sexual creation. And people adore the experience of sexual creation because that pure self feels so good. The pleasure and joy of good sex between two loving people feels as though something tangible and ecstatic is created. In the physicality of sex, brilliant, scintillating emanations charge the air with positive energy.

So we might also be able to view sexual creativity as:

- enlarging on and remembering valuable experience;
- opening up to good experiences, either real or imagined;
- sharing with the community the artist's (or lover's) own valid life experience;
- celebrating life in the shape of sexuality.

One of the reasons why Freud may have worked out only

part of the picture is because he left an important ingredient out of his version of psychology, which his rival and contemporary Alfred Adler thought to include. This ingredient is the need to feel connected to others, something that Adler called *gemeinschaftsgefühl*, or human interest. It is that sense of connectedness that enables us to revel in wonderful sex, to long to share feelings with others and to use the media of writing, painting and music to do precisely that.

Turning around the negative

That's all very well, you may say, but right now my sexual experiences are negative. How do I turn my sexuality around so that I read it more positively?

One approach is to look for important messages that your behaviour is sending. If you work from the premise that all behaviour has meaning, even behaviour that is termed 'bad', this makes the way that you live your sex life fascinating. If you can identify what your behaviour (or the behaviour of a partner) is telling you, you enrich your being. If all behaviour has meaning, there is no negative behaviour, only meaningful behaviour. By seeing your sex life as a form of creativity you gain a new perspective on it – however 'good' or 'bad' you consider it to be.

To give you an idea of how to do this, I am going to turn the tables on three sexual situations that are commonly defined as types of moral dilemma. I will attempt to interpret these dilemmas creatively.

I WHEN YOU HAVE SEX WITH SOMEONE YOU HARDLY KNOW
The negative interpretation is that sex with strangers is immoral. No nice person would have sex with someone they've only just met and such action tends to be viewed as the behaviour of someone desperate, over-needy, exploitative, reckless or feckless. All of which may be true but leaves out a lot of other explanations that are equally valuable.

A METHOD OF 'GETTING TO KNOW YOU' The positive interpretation says that even if you are having sex with someone you hardly know, sex can be the start of a process of showing this new person a special, inner you. And this can be true, regardless of who the partner is, be s/he prostitute, swinger or simply new friend.

A METHOD OF 'GETTING TO KNOW YOURSELF' What's more, sex is also a process of showing *you* the inner you. How else can you know what you are like in differing sexual circumstances unless you experience them? The difference between you and others (who do not act in the same way) is that you have courage to experiment and they do not.

A CHILDHOOD METHOD OF EMOTIONAL SURVIVAL How you first get to know someone sexually may be due to the kind of emotional survival beliefs you developed while you were growing up. If you were starved of love and affection in your formative years you may not only be needy for

these in adulthood, you may be greedy too. Your unconscious may have figured out that if you don't grab it as
soon as it's available, you may not get the chance again.
'Go for it and don't waste time on the preliminaries,' is
what your inner child is telling you. Your internal logic is
trying to protect you against isolation and desolation. And
sex is commonly misunderstood to be love and affection.

Your unconscious here is working on the survival patterns that it learned in infancy. But when we work things
out for ourselves as little children, sometimes we get things
wrong. Or even if we didn't get it wrong at the age of four,
it may not actually be relevant 20 years later. So although
sex with complete strangers may feel instinctively comfort-
ing at one level, such a direct approach may bring as many
problems as solutions.

ACCEPTING YOUR DIRECT APPROACH Fortunately, such an
insight can be used in many ways. You may decide that you
are happy with your direct approach to sex and that this is
your own, very personal method of getting to know someone. The sex act can indeed act as a shortcut, assisting you
to know someone on an inner level. You can learn things
from sex. You can discover, from the way another
expresses him/herself, whether s/he is tender, abrupt,
thoughtful, or selfish. All of this information can be seen in
body language, through verbal skills, as a result of eye
movements. In the short space of a 15-minute encounter

you can understand if you really want to develop a relationship with this person or not.

As long as the other person can deal with this, such an approach can lead to a loving and enduring relationship. I know couples who met through going to swinging parties, whose first introduction was during sexual intercourse. By puritanical standards they should have gone straight to hell, definitely not have been able to score a bull's-eye with a new relationship. Yet they liked each other so much that they started dating. They carried out courtship backwards and ended up moving in together. If you can manage to lose the judgemental attitudes that you were almost certainly brought up with you begin to see that there are many distinct possibilities for life that cannot be taken on board by an inflexible mind.

MODERATING YOUR DIRECT APPROACH. On the other hand you may feel that your tendency instantly to jump into bed is beginning to harm you. You may prefer to slow your sex life down but find it difficult to do because all your instincts goad you to do otherwise. Trying not to have sex can feel surprisingly risky: as though you will be rejected, as though nobody will like you, even as though you may never find a partner. This is a tough set of feelings to overcome. But it can be done! There are several methods of moderating the anxiety you feel when you draw back from instant sex.

Next time you find yourself about to bundle into bed,

stop for a minute, remove yourself to the bathroom and look at your face in the bathroom mirror. Now repeat the mantra '*I am* OK *without sex*' several times. If you still find yourself inclined to zip off to the nearest king-size, look at the fingers on your right hand and wiggle them one by one as you repeat the mantra.

Tell your partner that you think s/he is gorgeous but you do not yet feel comfortable with them. Suggest instead that you meet for a further date because 'you would really like to get to know them better'. If the new friend is going to be halfway suitable they will play ball with this suggestion. If they don't, they are wrong for you – not you for them. And any time you feel a resurgence of that anxiety, wiggle the fingers of your right hand and say '*I am* OK *without sex.*'

If the anxiety still persists, think of something you really like to wear, such as a pair of favourite shoes, and go straight to the wardrobe and put them on. By substituting a mantra or your favourite shoes for your needy anxiety activity you will start to feel better. Finger-wiggling sounds daft but it's a simple version of strategic therapy. Strategic therapy was an invention of Milton Erikson; he recognised certain behaviour as 'looping' – a circular argument that goes round and round but never gets resolved. Certain patterns of behaviour such as a marital row can 'loop'. He advocates doing something out of the ordinary that distracts you from the 'looping' and on many occasions is

daft enough to make you see the crazy pattern you've been trapped in. One famous example was the couple who were under his orders to go upstairs to the bathroom every time they started rowing and sit, fully clothed, in the bath. The strategy worked.

Look for the positive aspects

We have looked here at the positive side of the dilemma. Anyone can do the same. And there are good reasons for opening the mind to affirmative types of sexual approach. It is supremely unhelpful to tell people that something is wrong with them. Not only is any advice rejected out of hand but enough additional anger may be engendered to compound the behaviour.

On the other hand, looking for and finding out what is relevant works. Then people will listen, they feel good, they feel relaxed enough to take in any constructive approaches subsequently put forward. When they can feel that a sexual choice is their own and not something foisted upon them, they reach a position where they can take the responsible option that properly suits them, rather than suits the person advising.

2 Sex with yourself

How often have you heard the words 'Oh, he's a sad wanker'? Part of our Victorian inheritance is to believe that there is something weak, harmful or immature about mas-

turbation. Anthony Storr, for example, in his book The Dynamics of Creation, *states that self-stimulation acts as a short circuit – instead of relating to the real world, it throws the masturbator back on himself and effectively short circuits sex's connection with real life. His conclusion is that the masturbator is unlikely to produce any serious works of art because all his imagination will be channelled into his masturbation.*

A LOGICAL APPROACH Let's take a closer look at this self-rewarding sexual activity. Storr might also add, if we extend his argument, that the masturbator would be unable to make any serious relationship, since his imagination would still be channelled elsewhere. But, unless s/he is a complete obsessive, this is nonsense. You might as well argue that someone with a full heterosexual love life couldn't also be a great writer or composer – sexual intercourse occupying the same creative space as masturbation. Yet we know that this is nonsense. Picasso is an obvious example of a great creator who thoroughly enjoyed sex. Mozart is another. Both intercourse and masturbation require energy and imagination and logically neither is a bar to creativity.

THE CELEBRATORY APPROACH I see masturbation as an extension of pure self – a method of expressing 'being' – I would see great art functioning in the same way. Far from any of these activities being sublimations, they can be wonderful methods of keeping in touch with your self-value, self-confidence and inner beauty. Masturbation is a basic, primitive and pure method of doing so. Instead of turning us inwards, masturbation can equip us for handling the world with equanimity.

MASTURBATION DEVELOPS THE IMAGINATION But masturbation is more than an expression of being. It is a training ground for the body, for getting to know your sexual response, for taking charge of your own sexuality. It offers information which can be brought into a relationship with a lover so that you can both feel unpressurised. Masturbation is a method of developing the imagination. It is a rescuer: it rescues its happy practitioners from lack of sensuality, from sexual frustration, and from boredom. It is a healer; it comforts in times of sadness, and feels good when you are without a partner.

WHEN SHOULD YOU STOP SOMEONE FROM MASTURBATING? A common sex problem focuses on the discovery by a loving wife that her husband is masturbating regularly. She reacts by feeling terribly hurt. She interprets his actions as meaning she is not enough for him. She may possibly be right. But she may also be completely wrong. If she sees his actions from his point of view rather than hers, she might find many perfectly innocent alternative interpretations. For example, he may be masturbating from time to time

purely because he likes it. And why shouldn't he? You
don't usually prevent a partner from eating chocolates, do
you? You understand his preference because you like
chocolate too. In fact, you are probably glad he is having a
great time feasting his taste buds.

It is possible to look on masturbation in the same non-
judgemental way as chocolate-eating. One way of doing so
is to keep an eye out for the positive aspects. What are
they? The masturbator probably has:

* a high sex drive;
* a versatile sexual imagination which you, as his/her
  partner, are lucky enough to benefit from when the
  two of you do enjoy sexual intercourse.

We don't own our partners even though sometimes we
would like to. They are separate people who, if we are
lucky, will enjoy journeying through life side by side with
us. One of the hardest tasks in marriage is to tolerate each
other's differences. Attitudes to masturbation may be one
of these. Your partner's attitude may be quite different
from yours. So the secret is to detach yourself from your
territorial instincts, cut out any suspicion that your partner's masturbation may reflect badly on you and look
instead for his/her true inner motivation.

Use empathy
In this dilemma I have suggested putting yourself into the

other person's shoes to get a true idea of his/her motivation. Learning to be empathic prevents us from becoming overly 'me-centred' and lets us see all sides of a problem instead of only our own entrenched or paranoid one.

3 Sex is an ecstatic experience

This is a moral dilemma in reverse. Although many people would like to believe that sex can be an ecstatic experience, this is often seen as an empty premise – the by-product of trashy romantic novels. Also, certain religious movements teach that the only true ecstatic experience is that of oneness with god. So the concept of ecstatic sex is a troublesome one for some people.

AN ORGASM IS ... JUST AN ORGASM. And very nice too! But very occasionally, by accident we get a glimpse of another reality. One way of doing so is through sex. It is the white light, the blinding flash, the projection out into a cool bright space, where for seconds only you experience pure ecstasy. And it does exist. But we have learned to distrust such an experience, to think of it as unreal, of no account, as some kind of fantasy put out into the ether by strange and ancient gurus.

WHO'S GOT TIME FOR SPIRITUALITY? We no longer associate ecstasy (of any sort) with our hurrying, scurrying twenty-first-century lives. We certainly don't want to credit sexual ecstasy as a serious possibility because if we do, we may have to acknowledge that there is something we haven't got, something missing. We are enormously grounded in today's reality, in the here and now. Perhaps we need to expand our spiritual consciousness, something which many people are now exploring. This is one way of doing it. Apart from which, who's got the time?

And yet ... if we think like this we may be defending ourselves from disappointment but we will also be limiting our possibilities. The edge to the kind of excitement termed ecstasy is a sense of true connectedness; there's an impression that through the amazing well-being that flashes across the brain we can somehow share that well-being; that if one of us experiences it so can anyone else. Even if this is an illusion, it is a particularly marvellous one. I have no doubt that the more of us who manage to suffer such an illusion the better.

HAVE STRENGTH – THINK SPIRITUAL So I would like to make a plea for at least considering the possibility that sexual ecstasy exists. I don't believe it is something we can experience very often. But the occasional fleeting glimpse is wonderful. I'm not even sure that any of the disciplines designed to lead towards it, such as Tantric sex, actually work. But if you analyse the ingredients of these disciplines, there's a valuable emphasis on time, peace, unhurried sensuality, and sharing.

You are right if you think there is nothing particularly new about sexual ecstasy. Ancient belief systems have taught it for thousands of years. Yet my guess is that the notion of sexual ecstasy upsets certain moralists. If everyone were busy aiming at white lights and pure peace, wouldn't the world go mad? Wouldn't it spiral out of control, upsetting all the great institutions that have ruled for the last 2000 years? So in order to avoid such moral chaos, the idea of sexual ecstasy has been quietly relegated to a backwater. It takes faith to persevere with an idea that has been downgraded. Nevertheless a return to some of the old beliefs, bringing to them the benefits of new technical knowledge, often helps us to make leaps of understanding.

TANGLING WITH TANTRA Those who are keen to explore sex in the brain might consider buying copies of the *Kama Sutra* or investing in Tantric sex manuals. Alas, the observation of a certain ritual does not ensure that you will reach heaven. But who knows? Perhaps you might. Much of what the manuals teach makes sense. To repeat, the ingredients of Tantric sex are time, relaxation, the cultivation of extreme intimacy, the slow, gradual build-up of desire and tactile sensation. If you follow the advice, you achieve a type of timelessness. And when sexual excitement and orgasm become timeless that's when ecstasy sets in.

HAVE FAITH IN YOUR INSTINCTS If you honestly believe

that you have been lucky enough to clock out to a karmic universe before arriving back on the bed in a tangle of sheets and duvets, don't be afraid. Explore this belief. It can't hurt anyone and it sure as hell beats cocoa for a bedtime experience. It is by considering and measuring our gut emotions that we enable ourselves to grow emotionally strong.

A brave new orgasm

For the benefit of doubting readers, let's look at why the world won't fall apart should you choose to tolerate – or even practise – the ideas put forward in this book. After all, there must be some risk, mustn't there? If people were allowed to do as they pleased sexually, they might wander naked in the streets and casually fuck in the nearest shop doorway. Surely the world as we know it would fall apart, wouldn't it? Wouldn't such behaviour mean we had reverted to an animal state? And if we became animal-like again wouldn't it mean the end of civilised intelligence? It's a doomsday scenario.

But I suspect that sex is a bit like fashion: there will always be people who want to be seen as different. These are the ones who will wear the contemporary equivalent of the emperor's new clothes, and who will make a point of being blatantly sexual. But there will also be some who want to be traditional, who would no more dream of having public sex than they would of going in for genital piercing. Thanks to the balance between the extremes and the 'trads', we wouldn't actually see huge differences. Far from civilisation falling apart, it would simply shift a little as it does anyway every couple of generations. We might achieve some public acceptance of outrageous sex style but we might also see more public rejection of it.

That slight shift in public opinion would probably hit us a little like computers have hit the attention spans of young people. Young men and women can take in a lot of material more rapidly than the preceding generation, provided it is served up to them in small bites rather than large tracts. This isn't the decline of civilisation, but it *is* change. Sexual ideas change too.

The inevitability of change

Change is almost the only thing that is inevitable. We are human, therefore we change. Simply by living and breathing we change. Surely it is better to tolerate and understand change rather than block it or attack it because we are frightened? Change is the very basis of any version of evolution.

Judging from the rapid rate of scientific discovery, our grandchildren and their descendants are due for some very remarkable choices where sexual options are concerned. On the basis of present technological development, here, in light-hearted fashion, are some of the sexual enterprises that could well evolve in the future.

CHANGE YOUR ORGASM Sexual libido (sex drive) has only very recently begun to be understood. It's not beyond the

realms of fantasy to envisage a future where you might decide if you want your orgasm to be long and dreamy, shallow and drifting, hard and intense, or rapidly explosive. How could you manage this? By taking a pill appropriately calibrated to release or inhibit sexual energy. Your pill pack might be packaged in all the colours of the rainbow, with violet and indigo for rapidly explosive orgasm, and yellow leading into white for shallow and drifting orgasm. The pills themselves would work on your excitement/inhibition brain centres but would also be boosted with graduated amounts of testosterone to provide additional sensitivity.

CHANGE YOUR SEX DRIVE If you hate the idea of swallowing pills containing substances that have to pass through your liver you might opt for one of the new booster sex gels designed to be rubbed directly on to the genitals. These gels would deliver sexual arousal directly to the penile or clitoral area, massively sensitising the area, and would also pass into the bloodstream, travelling up to the sexual brain centres. The end result: someone who turns on with anyone, under any circumstances. Such a gel would be invaluable to the many women who find it hard to experience orgasm. It would also work wonders for ageing men who experience less penile sensitivity and who therefore have problems turning on and sustaining an erection.

REMINDER: only 30 per cent of women can climax from intercourse alone.

CHANGE YOUR PHYSICAL SHAPE If you have enough money you can already do this, thanks to plastic surgery. In future, however, not only will you retain the option to totally resculpt your body but new preparatory drugs will ready the body to react well to the knife so that you can heal without scarring.

Hardly a month goes by without some new discovery made about drugs to prevent the human body from rejecting foreign tissue. It is becoming possible to graft all manner of organs on to human beings which, far from being rejected, appear to set like concrete. In future these spare parts may be grown from our own cloned cell nuclei, so that they would not be rejected as foreign tissue but would instead be welcomed as the body's own.

The sexual possibilities are major. From replacement genitals to somebody else's genitals, to extra genitals over and above the usual set, all of these transplants become logically possible. Imagine a woman with sensually enhanced breasts. By stroking and nibbling on her new sensi-breasts and sensi-nipples she could experience powerful climaxes any time she wanted. Imagine a male with an extra penis, specially designed to penetrate anally, at the same time as his usual penis penetrates vaginally. It's the sex aids industry gone twenty-first century.

CHOOSE THE SEXUALITY OF YOUR UNBORN CHILD And no, I don't mean the gender. I mean the sexuality – the degree to which any child may relate sexually. This would include their libido, their sensitivity, their easy arousal and their expression of sexuality. All it would take would be a small hormonal sexual success implant. So that there could be no danger of such a child being perversely exploited, the implant could be timed to come on at an appropriate age. In other words, you could ensure that your child would have no difficulties in enjoying a full sexual life as an adult even if you didn't manage it.

FUCK ONE PERSON Many of the problems with relationships arise from the fact that one partner (or even both) becomes sexually restless. Perfectly good marriages end because one member of the couple feels virtually compelled to explore the field. Imagine a world where, on marriage, you could choose the option of being bio-emotionally tailored to your spouse. What would this entail? You could choose to submit yourselves to a method of brain programming so that certain brain pathways regarding sexual attraction in both partners were induced to match perfectly and to focus specifically on each other. This would make it virtually impossible to stray.

The gain would be that many more couples would stay happy together. The loss would show up when one member of the partnership dies. We already see a widow/widower's version of this in the sex-therapy clinic where the bereaved individual wants to be sexual with his/her new partner. This person is indeed strongly attracted to the new lover but, when it comes to sex, remembers the deceased partner so automatically that sex in the present becomes impossible.

FUCK MANY PEOPLE SIMULTANEOUSLY Cybersex ultimately makes it possible not only to communicate by web-cam but also to wire your body into the internet system by virtue of electrodes attached to specific erogenous zones. This enables you and your partner to experience physical arousal even though you are making love at extreme long distance. One of the many benefits of this is that you can wire up to more than one individual at a time, a kind of chat bedroom so that you can take part in orgies.

The advantages would be massively increased sexual experience, particularly for people who might not otherwise enjoy a sex life. The disadvantage would be hard wiring – you might get so addicted to the chat bedroom that you couldn't leave it. Sad cases would be found holed up in their computer rooms, starved to death but having gasped their last with a look of intense pleasure on their face.

JOIN THE BORG. FUCK THE WORLD Trekkies will recognise the reference. For non-trekkies, the Borg is a race of half humans, half automatons who are all plugged into a global

invented by
DNA ~~kms~~
scientist

padlock

close up

touch-tone

brain. They are one of the interesting enemies created for humans to battle in the *Star Trek* TV series. They operate as a hive and roam the universe looking for other races to plug into their system so that their own brain expands and so that other races are enriched by the enormously varied experience that the Borg can provide.

It's not difficult to extrapolate from the kind of cyber-connections we will soon be able to make that there will be a real possibility of not only joining a small group for virtual sex but ultimately of joining an absolutely massive group for solar sex. Imagine a society where every member experienced their own and each other's orgasms simultaneously! They'd blow the top off the solar system.

The advantages? A massive increase of personal knowledge and orgasms so powerful they could knock you out for days. The disadvantages? Loss of personal identity and autonomy and the danger of group vulnerability where if one of you suffers so does everyone.

DOWNLOAD YOUR SEX Human beings may reach the stage of having a computer implant attached to the brain at a very early age. One by-product of this is that you could download your evening's sex directly from the internet. You have effectively become the Borg.

THE WORLD OF FLOATING GENDER Since our identities may be plugged into other people's brains at a young age we will find it difficult to remain fixed as either masculine or feminine – our actual experience will be of all genders. This means that not only would we have far greater tolerance of differing gender groups but that we might lose sight of our own gender and become free-floating. Put simply, we would be whatever gender was deemed appropriate for a particular sexual assignment.

THE CYBER ICE AGE Thanks to a cataclysmic event, the internet is destroyed, leaving the human race to flounder. Civilisation will be destroyed, millions will die and the human race will have to begin all over again. Only this time the great apes may hold the advantage over man since they will know how to survive in the wild. Man, on the other hand, will have virtually lost touch with reality.

Only kidding folks. Or am I?

Epilogue

We do have choices about how we can experience sex. We don't have to be channelled into whatever the current belief system puts out. If you go back to evolutionary premises, sex can be anything. It can be old brain – unconscious, instinctive – or it can be new brain – conscious, thoughtful. Either way of experiencing sex is 'real' and 'natural'. Which is why human beings would be wise to make the most of what they've got and if sex doesn't feel particularly satisfactory, try rethinking it.

Rethinking involves:

UNDERSTANDING MEMES – the power of ideas and where they come from. And considering floating a few memes of your own.

GETTING INSIGHT INTO YOUR BEHAVIOUR AND FEELINGS – this means understanding your family background and why you grew up with the personal 'survival' system that affects your sexual choices.

DECIDING IF YOU REALLY WANT TO CHANGE – or does your present situation in fact suit you?

MAKING SMALL CHANGES – if that is what you want. Make them gradually but persistently.

TAKING A SHOT AT CHANGING YOUR SEXUAL ATTITUDES – start off with our mini attitude-restructuring section. You could consider subscribing to one of the bigger ones in San Francisco or starting your own SAR group where you discuss sexual attitudes so that you can get much more comfortable with all aspects of sex.

MAKING A POINT OF SEEING THE OTHER SIDE OF A SEX PROBLEM – take a look at what the problem is telling you about yourself and your relationship.

WORKING CONSCIOUSLY ON FEELING HAPPY – appreciate what you have rather than focusing on what you lack.

TAKING ON BOARD THE HISTORICAL PERSPECTIVE – recognise the fact that every generation feels slightly different about sexuality and behaves accordingly.

DELIBERATELY LOOKING AT YOUR SEX LIFE AS IF THE GLASS WERE 'HALF FULL' – appreciate the creativity that goes into your every sex act and the subtlety of what you have already established with your partner.

WORKING ON FEELING UNAFRAID – pursue the sexual lifestyle that is right for you.

There are no standards for good sex in your brain. Sex is purely what *you* make it. On the other hand, if you remember the story of the moon orbiting the sun, sex is always, well, just sex.

Bibliography

Bagemihl, Bruce, *Biological Exuberance*, St Martin's Press, New York 1999

Bancroft, John, *Human Sexuality and its Problems*, Churchill Livingstone, Edinburgh, London, Melbourne and New York 1989

Blackmore, Susan, *The Meme Machine*, Oxford Univesity Press, Oxford 2000

Evans, Dylan and Zarate, Oscar, *Introducing Evolutionary Psychology*, Icon, London and New York 1999

Hawes, Clair, *Couples Growing Together – a marriage enrichment program*, Coast Centre for Mediation and Counselling, Vancouver 1997

Holford, Jeremy and Hooper, Anne, *Adler for Beginners*, Writers and Readers, London and New York 1998

Hooper, Anne, *The Body Electric*, Virago, London 1979

— *Kama Sutra*, Dorling Kindersley, London and New York 2000

— and Perring, Michael, *Get Fit, Feel Fantastic*, Carroll and Brown, London 2000

Kinsey, Pomeroy, Martin, *Sexual Behaviour in the Human Male*, Saunders, Philadelphia and London 1948

Lovell, Mary, *A Rage to Live: A Biography of Richard and Isabel Burton*, Norton, New York 2000

Masters, William and Johnson, Virginia, *Homosexuality in Perspective*, Little, Brown and Co, Boston 1979

Miller, Geoffrey, *The Mating Mind*, Heinneman, London 2000

National Sex Forum, SAR *Guide for a Better Sex Life*, National Sex Forum, San Francisco 1977

Rose, Hilary and Rose, Steven, *Alas Poor Darwin*, Jonathan Cape, London 2000

Stopes, Marie, *Married Love*, reprinted by Phoenix Press, 2000

Storr, Anthony, *The Dynamics of Creation*, Penguin, London 1972

Wellings, Kaye, *et al*, *Sexual Behaviour in Britain*, Penguin Books, London 1994

Appendix

For more information on Sexual Attitude Restructuring courses write to the Institute for the Advanced Study of Human Sexuality, 1523 Franklin Street, San Francisco, CA 94109, USA

Tel: (415) 928-1133 Fax: (415) 928 8061

For self-teaching material on how to experience orgasm, look out for *The Body Electric* written by myself (see below) and available mail order from PO Box 29742, London NW3 1FE. Cheques for £10.00 (including postage and packing) made out to Anne Hooper.

Acknowledgements

To my colleagues Jeremy Holford-Miettinen and Dr Michael Perring for the information and stimulation they have supplied on the subject of sex and evolution.